Happy Venture
Book Four

Holiday Time

FRED J. SCHONELL

Illustrated by Rees Roberts
and Kiddell-Monroe

OLIVER AND BOYD : EDINBURGH

Note on the Revised Edition

HAPPY VENTURE was conceived and has been validated as a basic teaching method, and as such has proved outstandingly successful. Our language is a living one, however, and so certain expressions appearing in the original edition have now gone out of use.

Before his death in 1969, Professor Schonell was actively engaged in discussion with the publishers about the revision of the entire series. Unfortunately he was not able to undertake this before he died.

After consultations with practising teachers throughout the country and abroad, it became apparent to the publishers that the principles on which the series was based had not altered, but that minor changes to up-date the text could be made without affecting the well-tested structure of the series.

Accordingly, in this book, teachers will find:

new illustrations where main characters appear; up-dating of text where required and consequent alterations to Word List.

The publishers acknowledge the help and advice of Miss Angela Ridsdale of Toorak Teachers' College, Malvern, Victoria, Australia, in the revision of this series.

OLIVER AND BOYD
Tweeddale Court, Edinburgh
A Division of Longman Group Ltd.

First Published 1959
Twelfth Impression 1970
Revised Edition 1971
Reprinted 1972
ISBN 0 05 002382 9

© 1971 The Executors of the late Sir Fred J. Schonell

Printed in Great Britain by
T. and A. Constable Ltd., Edinburgh

Contents

Off for the Holidays   1

At the Seaside   12

Bombo, the Elephant   19

The Merry-Go-Round   28

How Dick and Malcolm Saw
the Circus   30

The Nasturtiums that Were Too
Proud for their Boots   41

Joey, the Kangaroo   60

We See the Ships   71

Down Goes a Lifeboat   79

The Picnic   86

Good-bye, Seatown!   91

The Last Day of the Holidays   95

Ming, the Panda   97

The Chimpanzees' Tea Party   99

Small Silver Bear who Slid from
the Sky   104

Off for the Holidays

"The holidays are here,
the holidays are here," cried Dick,
as he came running home from school.
"The holidays are here, and we shall
soon be off to the seaside."

"Yes," said Mummy, "but we must
get our cases ready in time."

"We shall help with the cases,"
said Dick and Dora. "We shall get
the cases ready for the holidays."

"Thank you," said Mummy.
"Dick, will you please find
your bat and ball, and see
that your bucket and spade are ready?"

"Yes, Mummy," said Dick.
"I shall get my bat and ball
and my bucket and spade now."

"Dora, you can help me with the
cases. Put your big red ball in a case
and then clean your shoes, please."

"I can't find my spade, Mummy,"
said Dick. "I've looked and looked."

"I think it's in the garden,"
said Mummy.

After some time Dick found his spade
in the garden, and at last the cases
were ready for the holiday.

Next morning Dick and Dora
were up early.
Mummy and Daddy were up early, too.

" Now, Dick," said Daddy.
" Will you please take Fluff and Nip
to Mrs. Smith? She will look after them
while we are away."

At ten o'clock a taxi came to take
them to the station.

Daddy took two cases.
Mummy and Dick had one case each,
while Dora took a small bag.

They all got into the taxi.

Soon they came to the station.

"May I get the tickets, please?" said Dick.

"Yes," said Daddy. "Take this money."

"There are four of us going to Seatown," said Dora, "so we shall want four tickets."

"Yes," said Daddy, "ask the ticket man for two and two half returns to Seatown. A return ticket will bring us home again."

"Two and two half returns to Seatown, please," said Dick.

"Here you are," said the man. "The train will be in very soon."

Dick gave the tickets to Daddy.

They walked along the platform with the cases, and waited.

Dick looked along the lines.

" The signal is down," said Dick.
" The train must be near now."

" Here she comes," cried Dora. " I can
see the engine coming up the hill."

When the train came into the station
Daddy asked, " Is this the train
for Seatown ? "

" Yes, this is it," the porter said.

So they all got in, and Dick and Dora
each had a seat by the window.

5

The train was soon out of the town.

" What a lot of cows there are
in the fields," said Dick.

" Yes, and a lot of horses, too,"
said Dora.

" I know what we shall do," said Dick.
" You count the cows you see,
and I shall count the horses I see."

" One, two, three," counted Dora,
as the train raced along.

6

" Four, five, six, seven,"
Dora counted again.

" Where are they ? " cried Dick.

" Over there on that hill," said Dora.

" Oh, yes," said Dick. " I see four cows.
Three and four make seven.
You have counted seven, Dora."

" Now it is my turn," he said,
as he counted three horses
near a farm house.

In the next field Dora counted
five red cows and five black ones,
but Dick soon made up for that.

"Look, look!" he cried.
"Look at the soldiers!"

They all looked out of the window
and saw soldiers marching along the road.

They were singing as they marched
along, and Dora said,
"I know what they are singing.
We sing that song at school. It is
called 'The Grand Old Duke of York.'

The grand old Duke of York,
He had ten thousand men.
He marched them up to the top
    of the hill,
And he marched them down again.
And when they were up, they were up,
And when they were down, they were
    down,
And when they were only half way up
They were neither up nor down."

"Oh, that's a grand song,"
said Daddy.

" We can all sing that with Dora,
and then we shall all be soldiers."

So they sang the song again :

" The grand old Duke of York,
He had ten thousand men.
He marched them up to the top
    of the hill,
And he marched them down again.
And when they were up, they were up,
And when they were down, they were
    down,
And when they were only half way up
They were neither up nor down."

Dora said, " We have lots of fun
at school when we sing that song.
When we say the lines :

' He marched them up to the top
    of the hill,'

we all march along as if
we were marching up a steep hill.

9

And when we say the line :

  ' And he marched them down again,'

we all turn round and march
like soldiers coming down a hill."

  As Dick looked out of the window again
he saw that some of the soldiers
were riding in twos.

  Dick counted quickly by twos.
" Two, four, six, eight, ten, twelve,"
he cried.

  " Oh, that was good," said Dora.
" I'm glad you counted so many."

And so the game went on.

As they reached the seaside
Daddy said, "Did you win, Dora?"

"Yes, I won by five," said Dora.

"Seatown! Seatown!"
cried the porter at the station.

Quickly they took the cases
out of the train.

"This way out," Dick read at the gate.

"Tickets, please," said the ticket man.

"I must break each ticket," said Daddy.

"What is that for?" asked Dick.

"One half of the ticket is to take us
home again," said Daddy. "I shall give
the other half to the ticket man.
Now let us find the house
where we are to stay for the holidays."

Mummy, Daddy, Dick and Dora
got into a taxi and went to the house.

At the Seaside

" Here are your bucket and spade."
Mummy said to Dick. " You and Dora
may go on to the beach."

" Oh, this is great ! "
shouted Dick and Dora,
as they ran down to the sands.

Dick looked about the beach.
He was looking
for some nice clean sand.

" Here we are, Dora," he said.
" Let us make a castle.
You can help me to make a castle
in the clean sand.
You dig with the spade while I make
it up with buckets of sand."

They quickly made a castle
of clean, white sand.

" It looks great," said Dora.

" It's only half made yet," said Dick.

"Now, we must find some shells.
The shells will do as windows
for the castle," said Dick.

"I shall look for some bits of wood.
We can put wood for the doors.
If you can find some sticks, Dora,
they will do for soldiers.
Then we must dig a moat
around the castle.

"I shall dig the moat with the spade
while you bring some water
in the bucket to fill the moat."

At last they finished the castle
and it was time to go home.

Next morning Dick and Dora
were up early. After breakfast
they went down to the beach again.

" Oh," said Dora,
" the sea is far away."

" Yes," said Dick, " the tide is out.
See how wide the sand is to-day.
Look, there are pools of water
in the sands by the sea. Let us see
what we can find in the pools."

Dora found a shell like a fan.

" Here is a little fish
in this pool," said Dick.
" We shall catch the fish
and put it in the bucket."

" Yes," said Dora, " then we can bring
it down to the beach each day,
and give it clean sea water."

" Look, there's a bird near that pool,"
cried Dora.

" It is a sea-gull, but it cannot fly.
It can only run," said Dick.

The sea-gull ran along the beach.
Dick ran after it and took it
in his hands.

" Why can't it fly? " asked Dora.

" Look, there is oil on its white wings."

" How did it get the oil
on its white wings, Dick? "

" The oil gets on to the water
from the ships. When the sea-gull
swims in the oily water it gets
the oil on its wings. I will
take the sea-gull to Daddy," said Dick.

" Yes," said Daddy, " it has oil
on its wings, but it is not very bad."

Daddy got the oil
off the sea-gull's wings with a towel.

" Now its wings are clean," he said.

So Dick and Dora took the sea-gull
back to the beach and set it down
on the clean, white sand.
It ran along the beach
and then flew up into the sky.

" Squee, squee," it said.

" It is saying,
' Thank you for getting the oil
off my wings '," cried Dora.

16

" Now," said Dick, " let us make
a ship of sand." They began to dig.

" Hullo, Dick !
Hullo, Dora ! " someone called.

Dick and Dora turned round quickly.
It was their friend, Malcolm Brown.

" Hullo, Malcolm," cried Dick and Dora.
" Where have you come from ? "

" We are having a holiday here,
at the seaside," said Malcolm.

" We are glad to see you," said Dick.
" Come and help us make this ship."

When the ship was finished,
Dick, Dora and Malcolm had
a fine game on the beach.

Then Malcolm went with Dick
and Dora to their home.

" Here is Malcolm," cried Dick,
as they reached home.

" Hullo, Malcolm," said Dick's father.
" We are glad you are here
for the holidays. Please ask your mother
and father to come and see us
to-night."

Dick and Dora were getting ready
for bed, when Malcolm's father and
mother came.

" Hullo, Mrs. Brown! Hullo,
Mr. Brown!" cried Dick and Dora.

" Mr. Brown, please tell us a story
before we go to sleep," said Dick.

" Yes, a story, please," said Dora.

Bombo, the Elephant

" What kind of a story do you want? "
asked Malcolm's father.

" Do you know a story
about an elephant? " said Dick.

" Yes. I know one
about an elephant. It is called
'Bombo, the Elephant '."

Bombo was a big elephant more than
twenty years old. He had
a very long trunk and very wide ears,
but his eyes were only small.

He could pull heavy cases along
or break a small tree in half.

A man named Kip looked after Bombo.
Kip and Bombo were very good friends.
Kip looked after Bombo well and
in return Bombo worked very hard
for Kip.

Each day Kip took Bombo
to the woodyard to pile up
heavy logs of wood.

Bombo would take a log of wood in his
trunk and swing it on to the pile.
Bombo made half the pile of logs
in the morning, and then finished
the other half of the pile
in the afternoon.

He made a high pile of logs, for he
wanted to go to the river when
he and Kip had finished their work.

Bombo liked to swim in the river
when the days were hot.

Each day after Bombo had piled logs
of wood in the woodyard,
Kip said to the big elephant,
" Do you want to swim ? "

Bombo said, " Umph ! Umph ! I do ! I do ! "
and Kip took him to the river.

Bombo would take Kip in his trunk,
swing him off the ground and then
let him get up on his wide neck.

21

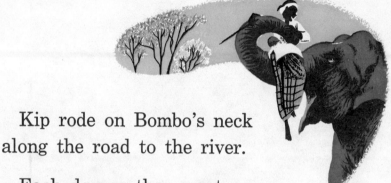

Kip rode on Bombo's neck
along the road to the river.

Each day as they went
along the road to the river,
they came to a tailor's shop.
Here Bombo stopped
and his eyes twinkled.

The tailor sat,
with his legs over each other,
making a coat. He looked up.

" Hullo, tailor," said Kip.
" Have you worked hard to-day ? "

" Yes, I have been working all day,'
said the tailor.
" Has Bombo worked hard to-day ? "

" Yes," said Kip, " he has piled
many logs in the woodyard to-day."

" Then I must find him something
to eat," said the tailor.

And what do you think Bombo did ?
He put his trunk into the shop
and the tailor gave him a bun.

Bombo took the bun in his trunk
and put it into his mouth.

" Thank you very much," said Kip.

23

Bombo and Kip then went down
to the river. Here all the elephants
were rolling and splashing
in the cool water.

Bombo walked into the river
and rolled and splashed.
He took water in his trunk
and squirted his back. He squirted
other elephants, and they squirted him.

One hot day Bombo had worked hard
in the woodyard, and Kip
and he were going to the river.
They reached the tailor's shop, but
this day his friend, the tailor, was out.

One of the tailor's men saw Bombo
put his trunk into the shop.

" What do you want ? " said the man.

Bombo's eyes twinkled as he
put his trunk near the man.
He thought of the nice bun
that the tailor always found.

But the man thought he would
play a trick on Bombo.
So he pricked the end
of Bombo's trunk with a pin.

Bombo cried out and took
his trunk away quickly.

With a loud cry he started
down the road to the river.

" Don't cry," said Kip.
" Don't cry, Bombo."

But Bombo was angry. He ran into
the river and rolled over and over.
He squirted the cool water
hard on to his back.
He squirted and splashed
the water over the other elephants.

But as he left the river
Bombo went to a pool of dirty water
and filled his trunk with dirty water.
Then, with Kip on his back,
he started along the road again.

He stopped at the tailor's shop.
He waited for a little while
and the tailor's man came out.

" Why have you returned ? " he cried.
" What do you want ? "

Bombo did not talk. He was still angry.
He put his trunk near the man.
Then he squirted the dirty water
all over the tailor's man.

"Oh! Oh!" cried the man.
"It's wet. I'm cold. Stop! Stop!
I will not prick you again!"

But Bombo and Kip only laughed as
the dirty water went all over the man.

The Merry-Go-Round

Next morning Dick and Dora were going to another beach near Seatown.

Mummy said that their friend Malcolm could go with them to the other beach.

At the other beach they saw a merry-go-round.

" Oh, Mummy, may we have a ride ? " cried Dick and Dora.

" Yes," said Mummy, " but you must hold on hard."

" Five new pennies," cried the man. " Only five new pennies a ride ! "

" Here are five new pennies, Dick. Here are yours, Dora. Here are five new pennies for you, Malcolm," said Mummy. " You may all go on the merry-go-round."

" Pennies, please," said the man.

" I am going to ride in a boat,"
said Dora.

" I am riding a horse," said Dick.

" So am I," said Malcolm.

" Are you ready ? " cried the man.
" Hold hard. Off we go ! "

The music started.
The merry-go-round started,
and they went round and round.

How Dick and Malcolm Saw the Circus

After they came from the merry-go-round they met Malcolm's mother. She went with Mummy and Dora to the shops.

Dick and Malcolm went to see some men getting ready for a circus.

" I would like to go to a circus," said Dick.

" So would I," said Malcolm.

They saw the men bringing hay for the elephants.

" Hullo, boys," said one man. " Would you like to help us ? "

" Yes, please," said Dick and Malcolm.

" First bring some water for the elephants," said the man.

Dick and Malcolm took many buckets of water to the elephants.

" Now you can take more buckets
of water to the horses,"
said the circus man.

" What fine horses," said Malcolm.

" Yes," said Dick.   " How I should
like to ride on that pony."

" His name is Tony," said the man.
" We have seven more ponies like him."

31

Next, Dick and Malcolm saw a man
feed the seals with fish. He threw
fish to each of the seals in turn,
and they caught them in their mouths.

If a fish dropped into the water
the seal could jump in and get it
in a flash.

" See the baby seal," said the man.
" He is only one year old.
He claps his flappers
when the other seals do tricks.
We have seven seals in the circus.
What a splash they make when they
all jump into the water."

As the boys stood in front of the seals
the first man came over to them.

" Oh ! Here you are," he cried.
" Could you come to the circus
to-night if I gave you tickets ? "

" I shall ask Daddy," said Malcolm.

" I think we could come," said Dick.

" You would see the seals jumping
and the elephants, dogs and monkeys
all doing tricks. The ponies would
trot round while the music played,"
said the man.

" That would be grand," cried Dick.

The boys took their tickets.
" Thank you, thank you very much,"
they said, as they ran off quickly
to tell all about it at home.

" Come early,"
the man cried after them.
" Come early to get a good seat."

" Just look what I've got," cried Dick.
" A ticket for the circus!
A ticket for the circus!
May I go, Mummy? May I go, Daddy?
Malcolm has a ticket too."

" Yes, you may go to the circus
to-night," said Daddy.

Malcolm's father told him that
he could go to the circus too.

" The circus starts to-night
at eight o'clock," said Dick. " I do want
the clock to go round to eight quickly."

At last they set off for the circus.

Inside the circus there were
many people. The people were sitting
on rows and rows of seats, round
the circus ring. Each row was a little
higher than the other, so that people
at the back could see the ring well.

In the ring all the tricks were done.

As Malcolm and Dick took their seats,
two clowns came into the ring
and did some funny tricks.

" One of the clowns is the man
who fed the seals," said Malcolm.

" Yes," said Dick,
" how funny he looks now."

Then six ponies, driven by a woman,
came into the ring.

One clown had a small chair.
He jumped on a pony, put the chair
on its back and sat down on it.

" Get off," cried the lady
driving the ponies.
But the clown just laughed,
and started to read a book.

Then the lady cried,
" Up, ponies ! Up, ponies ! "

The ponies stood on their back legs
quickly and off rolled the clown
and the chair to the ground.
This made all the people laugh.

Next came the elephants. One elephant
rolled a ball along with his feet.
Another elephant sat on a stool.

" Hullo, Jumbo ! " said the clowns
to the third elephant.
" Come and play see-saw."

The clowns sat on one end
of the see-saw. Then quickly Jumbo sat
down on the other end, and
up into the air went the two clowns.

Dick said to Malcolm,
"I think I hear the seals coming."

Into the tent came the seals.

"Look at the baby one,"
said Malcolm.

Each seal sat on a stool.

"Now clap," said the man, and
all the seals clapped their flappers.

Then he gave each seal
something to do in turn.
One seal blew a trumpet. Another seal
beat a drum, while the other seals
kept balls on their noses.

When the seals had finished,
two ponies trotted into the ring
where the clowns were doing tricks.
Each pony had a little monkey
on its back.

" Ride quickly ! " cried the man,
and the ponies trotted quickly.

" Ride slowly ! " cried the man,
and the ponies walked slowly.

As each monkey passed,
he pulled off a clown's cap.

" Stop, stop ! " cried the clowns
as they ran quickly after the ponies.
But the monkeys made the ponies
go fast and the clowns could not
catch them.

The people laughed and clapped.
" Oh, how funny the monkeys are,"
cried Malcolm. " Just look, they are
putting on the clowns' caps now."

Then the music played, and, as
the ponies left the ring, each monkey
did a dance on the back of his pony.

When the ponies had gone from the tent,
three men did tricks
near the top of the tent in the air.

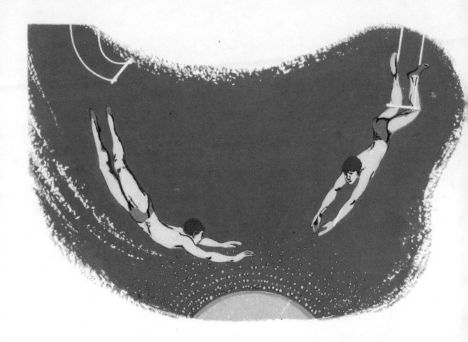

The men swung from small swings
tied up near the top of the tent.
Under the swings there was a net
to catch the men if they fell.

One man hung by his feet and swung
over to another man so that he could
catch him with his hands.

" That was very clever," said Dick.

At last the circus ended and
Dick and Malcolm went slowly home.

The Nasturtiums that Were Too Proud for their Boots

It was raining next day in Seatown, so Dick, Dora and Malcolm had to stay indoors.

Roderick came to see them. Roderick's father and mother had also come to the seaside for a holiday.

" What can we do while we are kept indoors by the rain ? " said Malcolm.

" Read or play trains," said Dick's mother.

" I know," said Dick. " We shall each read a story. Will you begin, Roderick ? "

" All right," said Roderick. " My story
is called ' The Nasturtiums that were
too proud for their Boots '."

"What are nasturtiums?" said Malcolm.

" Nasturtiums are pretty flowers
that grow up and up on sticks, or
alongside a house," said Roderick.

Then Roderick began his story :

Ben was the town shoemaker.
He was little and fat,
but he was a very good workman.
All the people of the town brought
their boots and shoes to Ben
to be mended.

Ben mended them and the people
gave him money. Sometimes the boots
were very old and had holes in them.
But Ben, sitting on his low stool,
would go ' Tap, tap; tap, tap; tap, tap '.
And soon the old boots were mended
nearly as good as new.

One day someone brought Ben
the oldest pair of boots he had ever
seen.

They had holes in them,
the heels were falling off,
and the sides were splitting.

Ben looked at the boots.
" I cannot mend these," he said.
" They are too old.
The heels are falling off
and the sides are splitting.

I could not mend
such an old pair of boots."

Then the man who brought
the old pair of boots was so angry
with Ben that he threw the boots
out of Ben's window into
Ben's back yard.

The man walked away, very angry.

There in the back yard the old boots
lay for a long time.
For weeks, and weeks, and weeks
they just lay in Ben's back yard,
and they began to get older,
and older, and older.

Now Ben liked flowers very much,
but he could not walk out into
the fields to see the flowers
as often as he would have liked to do.

He was too busy mending
people's boots and shoes.

One day he said to himself,
"If I can't go to see the flowers,
why shouldn't the flowers come to me?
Why shouldn't I grow some pretty
flowers for myself?"

"But," thought Ben, "I have no garden.
There is nowhere that I can grow
any flowers.
At the front of my shop is the street.
At the back there is only a back yard."

Ben went into the yard and began
to look around just to see if he could
find a spot where flowers would grow,
but there wasn't a spot anywhere.

" No, there's no ground here,"
said Ben to himself. " It's only
hard stones."

Ben turned to go back to his shop,
and just then he fell over the old boots.
Ben picked up the boots.
They were very, very old by now.
They had big holes in them,
the heels had nearly fallen off,
and the sides were so split that
you could see the inside of the boots.

" What old things they are," said Ben.
" The rain and sun have made
them break up like this."

But the old boots made Ben think.

" I know," he said. " I'll take
these boots to my friend's garden.
He will fill them full
of good, rich soil."

" Hullo, Ben," said his friend.
" What do you want ? "

"Oh," said Ben, "I want you to fill
these old boots full
of good, rich soil."

When the old boots were full of good,
rich soil, Ben took them home with him.
He put them in his back yard
near to the wall.

Out he went again
and bought some nasturtium seeds.

" Now," said Ben, " I shall plant
these nasturtium seeds in the
rich soil in the old boots."

He planted the nasturtium seeds
in the old boots, and put some of
the rich soil over them.

" Now," he thought to himself, " even if
I am too busy mending other people's
boots and shoes so that I cannot
go out and see the flowers growing
in the fields, I might have some
pretty flowers in my back yard.
I shall wait and see."

Soon the plants came up
out of the rich soil.

The plants in the right boot
looked at the plants in the left boot.

" What an old boot you have,"
said the plants in the right boot.

Then the plants in the left boot
looked at those in the right boot,
and said,
" Oh! You should
not talk. Just look
at your own boot.
It is full of holes."

Now the nasturtium
plants were proud
and did not like
their boots very much,
so they began to grow away
from them as quickly
as they could.

You could tell they were proud
for they held their heads as high
as they could.

" We must not stay
with those old boots," they said.
And they grew and grew,
taller and taller.

At last they reached the roof
of Ben's cottage.

" Now," they said,
" we can spread ourselves
out on the roof. It is time
to think about flowers."

So all the plants began to flower
and spread their flowers
over Ben's roof.

They were red and gold
and yellow and orange,
those nasturtium flowers, and they
just spread all over Ben's cottage roof.

Ben could no longer see the roof for
red, gold, yellow and orange flowers.

Early one morning the baker stood
looking out of his cottage on the hill,
above Ben's cottage.

The sun was shining on Ben's roof.
" Ben's house is on fire," cried the baker.

"Ben's house is on fire!"
shouted the baker loudly,
and, picking up a bucket
of water, he ran down the road.

As he ran towards Ben's cottage
to put out the fire, he saw the butcher.
"Ben's house is on fire," he shouted.

So the butcher picked up
a bucket of water and ran too.

They ran towards Ben's cottage;
they saw the shopkeeper.

"Ben's house is on fire," they shouted.

So the shopkeeper picked up
a bucket of water,
and also ran towards Ben's cottage.

Then the farmer and all his men
heard the shouts and saw the people
running towards Ben's cottage.
They picked up buckets of water
and ran too.

Then the farmer's wife and all
her maids ran too. Then the parson and
his wife and all his children ran also.
They all ran towards Ben's cottage
to put out the fire.

Faster and faster they ran, shouting,
" Ben's house is on fire!
Ben's house is on fire! "
And the water in their buckets
splashed out as they ran.

And the faster they ran the more
the water in their buckets came out.

Ben came out to see
what all the noise was about.

" Your house is on fire, Ben."

" Come out, Ben. You'll be burned."

" Look at the flames
all over your roof," all the people
shouted aloud.

Ben looked at his roof, then he looked
at the people running, and he looked
at their buckets, and he laughed.

He laughed so much that
he had to sit down
on the doorstep.

He laughed
till he had
to hold his sides.

He laughed
till his clothes
began to split.

Then he stopped.

" They're not flames," he said.
" They're nasturtiums. They're red,
yellow, gold and orange nasturtiums."

And he showed them the old boots,
and told them how the nasturtiums
did not like them. They were so proud
that they had climbed on to the roof.

" The red and the gold,
and the orange and the yellow
are not flames, but flowers," said Ben.

Then the baker laughed,
and the butcher laughed.

The shopkeeper laughed,
and so did the farmer and all his men.

The farmer's wife laughed,
and all her maids laughed too.

The parson and his wife
and all their children laughed.

They laughed so much that
they had to sit on the road to laugh.

They laughed till they had
to hold their sides with laughing.

They laughed till their clothes
began to split.

Then they stopped.

They looked again at the roof
of Ben's cottage, at the red,
yellow, gold and orange nasturtiums
shining in the sunshine.

They looked at each other and at
the buckets of water they had brought.

Then all the people said,
" What shall we do with
the water we have brought ? "

" Don't put it on my roof,"
said Ben, with a laugh.
" It's neither hot nor in flames."

" The old boots look very thirsty,"
said the parson.
" Let us give them a big drink."

So they put the water on the boots.
This was better than making
Ben's cottage wet.
And the old boots gave
the nasturtiums a drink. This was just
what the nasturtiums had been waiting
for up on the roof in the hot sunshine.

" Thank you," said the nasturtiums.

When the time came for the seeds
to be ready, the nasturtiums
threw some down to the old boots.

" Thank you," said the old boots,
" we shall look after them."

They put soil over the seeds
and kept them warm in winter, and when
summer came the seeds grew into plants.

Once again Ben's cottage
was bright with yellow, red,
orange and gold nasturtiums.

But this time the baker,
the butcher, the shopkeeper,
the farmer with his men,
the farmer's wife with her maids,
the parson and his wife,
and all their children didn't cry,
" Ben's house is on fire ! "
For they knew it was only Ben's
nasturtiums.

Joey, the Kangaroo

"I shall tell you a story
about a kangaroo," said Malcolm.
"It is about a Father Kangaroo
and a Mother Kangaroo. They lived
in Australia. Father Kangaroo
had a long tail and strong back legs.

He could hop very fast.

Mother Kangaroo had a long tail
and strong back legs.

She could hop very fast, too.

They had a baby Kangaroo.
His name was Joey and he looked like
a large ball of brown fur. His mother
kept him in a warm pocket of her fur.

Joey lived most of his time
in this big, warm pocket of fur,
in the front of his mother.

When Joey was inside this pocket of fur all you could see was his head sticking up.

Often just his ears were all you could see.

Each morning very early, even before
the sun had started to shine,
Father Kangaroo said,
" I know where we can find
nice, green grass with dew on it.
Shall we go and find some? "

So out they hopped to find some
nice, green grass with dew on it.

" Here you are,"
said Father Kangaroo.
" This grass has dew on it."

" Come on, Joey. Come on, Joey! "
called Mother Kangaroo.
" Jump out and have some green grass
with the early morning dew on it."

Up popped Joey's head and ears.
He jumped out of his pocket of fur
and ate some of the green grass.

Over by a tree Joey saw some long
bits of green grass.
How nice they were.

Every time Joey heard a noise,
like a bird singing or a rabbit
jumping, he ran back and jumped
into his mother's pocket of fur.

Father Kangaroo smiled;
so did Mother Kangaroo.

Sometimes Joey jumped so quickly
that he fell head over heels
into his pocket of fur, and then
all you could see was his tail
and a leg sticking out.

"Turn round, Joey,"
said Mother Kangaroo.
"I wish you would
stay out here
and stop playing
hide and seek
in and out of
your pocket of fur."

Joey turned round
and jumped out again.

" Oh, how hot the sun is now.
I am very thirsty, too,"
said Father Kangaroo. " I think we shall
find a cool place under the trees."

They had not been resting
very long in the cool place
under the trees when Father Kangaroo
pricked up his ears ; Mother Kangaroo
pricked up her ears, too.

She stood up on her strong back legs
and looked around.

" What's that ? " she said.

" Where, where ? "
cried Father Kangaroo, as he stood up
on his strong back legs.

" Near that fence under the trees.
Oh dear, they must be dogs,
and they are coming towards us ! "

" Then we had better run very fast,"
said Father Kangaroo.

Joey got right down into his mother's
warm pocket. No one could see him now.
Hop, hop, hop, went Mother Kangaroo.
Hop, hop, hop, went Father Kangaroo.

They made big jumps
on their strong back legs.

The dogs near the fence
saw Mother and Father Kangaroo
and off they ran towards them.

The dogs thought that they could
catch the Kangaroos very quickly,
but Father and Mother Kangaroo
could hop faster still
with their strong back legs.

Hop, hop, hop, they went.
Over the logs they hopped,
and over the fences they jumped.

The dogs had to find a place
to get through the fences,
but Mother and Father Kangaroo
could jump right over them.

Hop, hop, hop,
went Mother and Father Kangaroo,
but still the dogs ran after them.

"Joey is too heavy for me to carry,"
said Mother Kangaroo.
"What shall I do? I cannot hop
so fast with Joey in his fur pocket.
We must get him away from these dogs."

"I know," said Father Kangaroo;
"next time we come to a large bush
you must hide Joey in it very quickly."

"Yes," said Mother Kangaroo.
"How clever you are to think of that.
I will hide him in a large bush
and he will be safe from the dogs.
We can return for him
as soon as we have run
right away from these dogs."

So they looked out for a large bush.

"There," said Father Kangaroo,
"is a nice large bush."

Quickly Mother Kangaroo took Joey
out of the warm pocket of fur,
and put him into the large bush.

The dogs were too far away to see her.

" Keep still," she said to Joey.
" Don't make a noise
till we come back for you."

Joey knew that his mother and father
would come back for him
as soon as they could.

He heard them hop away
over the logs and over the fences.

Joey heard the dogs as they passed
the bush, and he kept very still.

The dogs ran hard after
Mother and Father Kangaroo,
but they could not catch up to them.

" Oh, they can't catch us now,"
said Father Kangaroo.

Soon he looked back and saw
that the dogs were a long way off.

Up in a tree a bird sang,
  " Hop, hop, hop !
  You must not stop,
  Till you win the race,
  And get back to Joey's place."

Mother and Father Kangaroo heard
the bird's song and they called back,
  " We won't stop,
  Till we win the race,
  And get back to Joey's place."

Mother and Father Kangaroo
ran faster still,
over more fences and logs and gates,
till they could not see the dogs
any more.

"Now," said Mother Kangaroo, "I think
we can go back for Joey."

They turned round and hopped back
towards the large bush
where they had left Joey.

When they reached the bush
Mother Kangaroo called,
"Joey, Joey."

"Here, here," shouted Joey.
"I'm safe in this big bush."

And with one big hop he jumped
right into his mother's pocket.

Away hopped Mother and Father
and Joey Kangaroo to find another
cool place under the trees.

We See the Ships

When Malcolm had finished his story
Roderick said, " Look, the rain has
stopped and the sun is shining brightly."

" Yes," said Dick's father, " but it will
still be wet on the sand. I think
it would be better to go to some other
place now.

" Who would like to see
the big ships this morning ? "

" Yes, yes," shouted Dick, Dora,
Roderick and Malcolm.
" Let's all see the ships."

" If we get some lunch ready," said
Mummy, " we can have a picnic
in the fields on the way home.
I will get cakes and bread and butter,"
said Mummy.
" Dora, will you please put some
cups in a case, then we can have
tea if we should get thirsty ? "

" Yes," said Dora, " we shall pack tea
and take some milk also.
Mr. Brown will make a fire to boil
the water, so we shall take a can."

Roderick said, " I shall go and ask
Daddy and Mummy if I may come, too.
I should like to see the ships."

The lunch for the picnic
was soon packed inside the cases.
When Roderick came back he said
that he could go.

Everyone went down the street
to wait for the bus.

Before long a green bus came
slowly towards them and stopped.

The boys sat in the front seats
while Mr. and Mrs. Brown and the
others sat at the back.

Roderick counted twenty people
in the bus.

Daddy gave Dora the money
to buy the tickets.

"Eight five new penny tickets,
please," said Dora to the conductor.

"Click! Click! Click!" went
the conductor as he made little holes
in the tickets.

The conductor gave Dora
eight tickets.

In twenty minutes they reached
the place where the ships
could be seen.

"Look, there are the funnels,"
said Malcolm.
"Can you see the masts, too?"

"I can see lots of funnels,"
said Dora. "Some are red, some
orange, some yellow, some green."

As they walked along
they counted twelve ships.
Eight were big ships and
the others were only fishing boats.

They walked near to the ships.

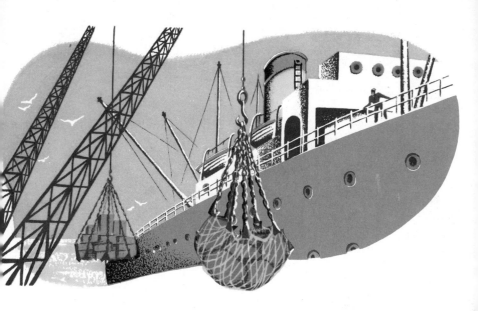

" We shall watch this one unloading all
kinds of things," said Mr. Brown.

Four cranes were working
near the ship.
The cranes were high up in the air.
One crane was unloading
cases of butter from Australia.

Another crane was unloading bags
of flour and wheat, and cases of eggs.

Mr. Brown told the boys to look up
into the air at the long wire
running over the wheels of the crane.

" Can you see the driver
at the window ? "

" Yes, yes," said the three boys.

" Watch the wire," said Mr. Brown.

Up, up came the wire
with a load of cases on the end.
Over it swung into the air,
and the driver let it down slowly.
Men quickly undid the chains around
the cases and up went the wire again.

After watching the cranes, Dora said,
" Oh, let us walk down to that ship.
It looks so clean and bright; it is
painted green and yellow."

" That is the biggest boat here," said
Mr. Brown. " It can take many people
far over the seas to many lands."

"Look at the port-holes,"
cried Malcolm. "I can see some people
through the port-holes."

" What big funnels and tall masts,"
cried Roderick. " What are the wires for
that go from one mast to the other? "

" Oh, they are radio wires,"
said Mr. Brown. " When ships are at
sea they can talk to each other and
to places on land by radio."

" Could we go on the ship? "
asked Dick.

" Wait here," said Mr. Brown. " I
shall ask if we may all look over it."

He returned to say that they could
go on the boat.

They went up the gangway
and an officer showed them where
the people sleep right through the night
just as if they were in their beds
at home.

They climbed down a ladder and
the officer showed them the engines
all clean and shining.

" We burn oil in the engines, and that
drives the propellers round
under the water."

" The propellers
drive the ship along," said Malcolm.

They climbed up the ladders again.

They went near the masts and funnels.

"How big the funnels are now!"
said Dora. "Are those
the radio wires?"

"Yes," said the officer,
"and these are the lifeboats.
We want the lifeboats sometimes
when we are at sea. The ship might
hit a rock and get a hole in it;
then we could reach land
in the lifeboats."

Down Goes a Lifeboat

Just then they all heard a noise.
Splash! Splash! They ran to the side
of the boat and there, in the water,
were two men. The men
had been standing on a ladder
painting the ship and
had fallen off the ladder into the sea.

" Out with the lifeboat ! "
shouted the officer.

Quickly a lifeboat with eight men
in it was swung over the ship's side.
Down, down it went
till it reached the water.

The two men in the water could swim.
It was not long before they were
picked up by the men in the lifeboat.

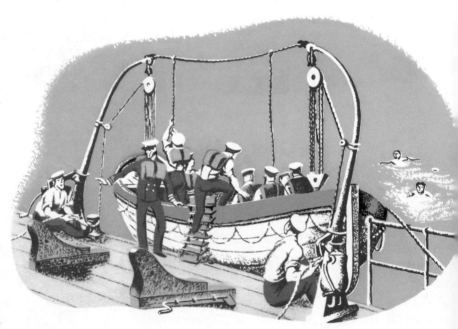

Everyone watched the lifeboat coming up.
Up, up it came as if it were tied
to a crane. In the lifeboat were
the two men who had fallen
off the ladder. They were wet through
and cold, but they had a warm drink
and put on dry clothes.

They were soon all right, and before
long they were on the ladders painting
once more.

" Now," said Daddy, " I think it is
time to go back to the bus."

As they walked towards the gangway
the officer said,
" Just look out there. Can you see
two tugs pulling a large ship ? "

" Oh yes," cried Dick. " Two small
black tugs pulling a big ship
with three funnels."

" Do let us stay to watch it," said Dora.

The tugs were small, but very strong.

" The tugs are pulling the boat
into a place near us," said the officer.

" Can you see a man at the wheel
of each tug ? " asked Malcolm's father.

The man at the wheel of the first tug
turned the wheel slowly.
The man at the wheel of the second tug
turned the wheel slowly.

The engines in the tugs drove
their propellers round fast and so
the big boat moved slowly onwards.

While the tugs slowly passed
in front of them the officer
pointed to the cliff at the far
end of a long beach.

The long beach went
far out into the sea.

" Can you see the lighthouse
up there? " asked the officer.
" A bright light shines
from there every night."

" What is the bright light for? "
asked Dora.

" That is to let the officers
on boats know where they are.
When they see the light
they know just which
way to go. If the light did
not shine so strongly we might
run on to the beach or
strike the rocks at night."

As they all looked over the sea
towards the tall stone lighthouse,
they could see many birds in the air.

" Why are there so many birds
in the air? " said Mrs. Brown.

" Oh, those are sea-gulls," said Daddy,
" and they are catching fish.
While a sea-gull is flying in the air
it can see the thousands of little fish
swimming in the sea below.

" When it sees a fish in the sea below,
down it flies as quickly as it can.
Into the water the sea-gull splashes,
and soon it has caught a fish."

Just then a sea-gull
flew over their heads.

As it turned in the air with its white
wings spread out, the shining sun
made it look like a silver bird.

Dora looked at Dick.

" Do you think that he is our sea-gull,
the one that had oil on his wings? "
asked Dick.

" Squee, squee! " cried the sea-gull.

" Oh, it must be our sea-gull,"
said Dick, and everyone laughed.

" Now," said Daddy, " I think
we should be going or we shall not have
time for our picnic.
Thank you very much, officer.
We are so glad that you have shown
us all over your fine ship.
We all liked our visit very much."

They all went down the gangway
and passed the cranes again.
Soon they could see only funnels
and the tops of masts once more.

" Good-bye, ships ; good-bye, fishing
boats ; good-bye, tugs and cranes ;
good-bye, lighthouse," said Dora,
Dick, Malcolm and Roderick.

The Picnic

" That red bus goes near the fields,"
said Dick, as they passed down a street.

" Quick," said Mr. Brown. " If we
run we shall catch it."

They caught the bus and once more
the boys sat in the front seats.

" Would you like to get the tickets
this time, Malcolm ? " said Dick's father.

" Oh, yes, please," said Malcolm.

Malcolm took the money and asked
the conductor for eight tickets.

" Click ! Click ! Click ! " went
the conductor as he cut little holes
in the tickets. The conductor
gave Malcolm eight tickets.

It was twenty minutes past one
when they got out of the bus
and walked through the fields.

Roderick said,
" Here is a good place for a picnic."

" This will be fine," said Mr. Brown,
" and we must also find a place to make
a fire and boil some water for tea.
Shall I show you how
to light a fire out of doors ? "

" Oh, yes," said the boys,
" let us help you light a fire."

" First, then, we must make a hole
in the ground," said Mr. Brown.
" Dick, you can do that.
There is something you can do, too,
Malcolm and Roderick. Please find
as many small dry sticks
as you can.
We want the sticks
to start the fire.
See that you get dry ones,"
he said. " They will
make the fire burn fast."

Roderick and Malcolm returned with lots of small dry sticks.

" Now," said Malcolm's father, " we want some paper."

Dick brought some paper from Mrs. Brown and put it in the hole.
Next they laid the small sticks across the paper.

" We must see that the sticks are not too near each other, so that the air can get through," said Mr. Brown.
" Malcolm, you can lay the next lot of sticks across. Put them across the other way this time, so that the air can still come through."

" The air goes up through the holes
between the sticks," said Roderick.

Mr. Brown said, " The last thing to do
is to lay some big sticks across,
so that the fire will keep burning
brightly."

" The fire will boil the water
for tea," said Malcolm.

" Now for a match from my pocket,"
said his father.

Dick lit a match and the paper
caught alight, then the small sticks
caught alight. Last of all,
the big sticks burnt up brightly.

" Hurrah, we have lit a camp fire,"
cried Dick, Roderick and Malcolm.

They put more sticks on the fire.

" The water will boil
now," said Dick.

Dora, Mrs. Brown and Mummy had
unpacked the cases and had spread out
a nice lunch on the green grass.

" This looks good," said Dick,
" and I do feel hungry."

" I'm hungry, too," said Dora.

" Stand aside everyone ! "
shouted Mr. Brown with a laugh.
" Here I come with
the boiling water for the teapot."

Once the tea was made they all sat
down to a good lunch.
When they had finished, Mr. Brown
said, " Now we must see that the fire is out.
No fire should ever be left to burn
after a picnic, for it might set fire
to the grass and burn the
farmers' wheatfields and trees."

When the fire was out
they packed their cases and caught
another bus home.

Good-bye, Seatown!

At last the holiday at the seaside
was coming to an end.

Dick and Dora went down to the beach
to play once more.

" I can nearly swim now,"
said Dora proudly to Roderick,
who was standing near by.
" Just watch me," she said,
going into the water.

" That's right," said Roderick.
" Move your arms and kick your legs
like a frog."

" Watch me," he said ; " I move
my arms and kick my legs
like a frog, too."

" Hullo," shouted Malcolm, " come
and get some shells with me."

Dick and Roderick helped Malcolm
to find some pretty shells.

"I am looking for a long piece
of seaweed to take home," said Dora.
"Daddy said to me: 'Bring a piece of
seaweed home with you and hang
it up. The seaweed will let you know
what kind of days we are going
to have—wet or fine.

When the piece of seaweed is dry
the days will be fine.

When the seaweed is wet and sticky
you know that there will be rain soon.'"

"Here is a long piece," said Dick,
laughing as he hung it
round Dora's neck.

"Here is another piece," said
Malcolm, and he put it round himself.

"Let us dress up in seaweed,"
cried Dick.

They hunted for long brown pieces
and long green pieces of seaweed
and hung them round their necks,
their legs and their arms.

" Let us do a seaweed dance,"
said Roderick.

Round and round they went till
they all fell over on the sand.

" It's getting late," said Dick.
" We must run back quickly."

Dora brought a piece of seaweed,
and they ran back to the house.

When they returned from the beach
Mummy and Daddy had packed
the cases once again.

" Now for the station," said Daddy.
Malcolm's mother and father, with
Malcolm and Roderick came to the
station to see them off. At the
station Daddy took the return half
of the tickets from his pocket and
showed them to the ticket man.

The signal went down and the train
came into the station. They all got in.
The train moved slowly away.

" Good-bye, good-bye," cried everyone.

The seaside holiday was over.

The Last Day of the Holidays

Daddy, Mummy, Dick and Dora
reached home safely from the seaside.
They were all glad to see Fluff
and Nip once more.

" What would you like to do to-day? "
asked Mummy. " It is the last day
of the holidays."

" I have a surprise! " said Daddy.
" We shall all go to the Zoo
and see the new panda."

" Oh, yes."
cried Dick and Dora together.
" We've been wishing someone would
take us to see the new panda."

" May we take May with us? "
said Dora.

" Yes," said Mummy. " Ask her now."

Dick packed some nuts
for the monkeys.

Then everyone caught a bus to the Zoo.

They reached the gates of the Zoo,
and Daddy went in first.
He gave some money to the man
at the gate and said,
" Two, and three children, please."

The man let them in one at a time
through a turnstile. The turnstile
went " click, click " each time
someone went through.

" Click, click," it said
as Dick went in.

" Hear it go ' click, click ' as I go
through the turnstile," said Dora.

When they were inside the Zoo
grounds Daddy asked a keeper,
" Where can we find the panda,
please ? "

And he showed them
the way to the panda.

Ming, the Panda

They came to the panda's cage
and there was Ming, the panda.

" Oh, how pretty she is," they all said.

Ming was rolling over and over
with her paws up in the air.

" She looks just like a big fluffy
teddy bear," said May.

" Yes," said the keeper,
standing near by,
" Ming has a teddy bear of her own,
made just like herself.
I shall put it in with her and you
can see her play with it."

The keeper put the toy panda
in the cage with Ming.
Ming took it in her arms
and rolled over on the straw.

" Oh, look ! " cried Dick. " She is biting
the toy panda's ear now."

Ming looked up at them as if to say,
" This is a grand game, isn't it ? "

" Doesn't she look funny with that
black spot over each eye ? " said Mummy.

" The Zoo has another panda,
called Tang," said the keeper,
" a friend for Ming."

The Chimpanzees' Tea Party

" Now we should say good-bye
to Ming," said Daddy,
" and walk quickly
to see the chimpanzees' tea party.
The chimpanzees have their
tea party at four o'clock."

They walked quickly along to
a place where a table and chairs
had been put ready on the green grass.

Many people were waiting to see
the chimpanzees' tea party.

A keeper who stood near Daddy said,

" They won't be long now, that is
if they haven't got out of their cages.
Last week we were just getting ready
for the chimpanzees' tea party
when a woman came to us.
She said, ' As I was coming along
on a bus I saw eight chimpanzees
playing on the roof of a house.'

" Three keepers ran off
as fast as they could,
and there were four chimpanzees
out on the roof of a house.

" The other four chimpanzees
were inside the house.

" They had all got out of their cage
by pulling away a piece of wood
from a hole in front of the cage.

" They all went into a house near by,
and while four of them climbed out
on to the roof the other four
chimpanzees stayed inside.

" And what a game they had !
They turned over a box full of eggs.
They upset all the tables and chairs.
They turned on all the lights
and left all the taps running.
They also found some bags of flour
with which they hit each other.

" When the keepers came, the four
chimpanzees were white all over
with flour.

" They did look funny.
They had flour everywhere, all over
the house, on their heads, on their
arms and legs, and even in their eyes.

" The keepers cleaned the flour
off them and led them by their paws
back to their cage.

" The chimpanzees laughed at each other
and at their keepers.

" The other four chimpanzees came
down from the roof.

" They ran over the road and sat
on top of a turnstile. People stood
watching them till the keepers came."

Just as the keeper finished his story,
four chimpanzees sat down at the table.
Each chimpanzee was given
a cup of water, and each one had
a plate of carrots, turnips, apples
and green foods.

They ate with spoons.

One chimpanzee named Booboo
took a piece of apple from
another's plate.

" Stop that, Booboo," said the keeper.

When the keeper was giving them
more water, a young chimpanzee
named Jubilee stood on the table
to hold up his cup.

" No," said the keeper, " not till you
sit down."

It was Jubilee, too, who got
a smack on the paw
when he took two pieces of cake.

After they had finished eating,
the chimpanzees came round
to beg for pennies.
They gave the pennies to the keepers.

When the chimpanzees had been taken
back to their cages, Daddy and Mummy
took the children to see the seals
and the elephants. And soon it was
time to go home.

Small Silver Bear who Slid from the Sky

It was five o'clock when they got home.

" Just in time for Story Time,"
said Dick, as he turned on the television.

" Now to-day," said the television
man, " I shall tell you another Zoo
story, about a Small Silver Bear."

He lived with the Moon,
the Small Silver Bear.

No one knew where he came from,
and by the time Small Silver Bear
had reached the Moon, he himself
had forgotten. He just stood there
on the white, fluffy cloud and smiled.

" Where did you come from ? "
asked the Moon in surprise.

Small Silver Bear looked surprised, too.
" I don't know," he said.

" What do you want ? " asked the Moon.

Small Silver Bear put his ears back,
twiddled his paddy paws and smiled
again. Then he curled up beside
the Moon and went to sleep.

And there he stayed.
The Moon grew fond of him and
Small Silver Bear soon forgot that he
had ever lived in any other place.

He was very happy.
He played with the stars, slid down
the moonbeams and bounced up and
down on the clouds.

In the daytime the Sun told him
stories. At night his friend the Moon
shone on his silvery coat and told him
that he could stay there for ever.

" I will," said Small Silver Bear.
" I'll stay for ever and ever."

And so he might have done
if he had not been so fond
of sliding down moonbeams.

Every night he did it.
He would sit down on the nearest one
and go sliding down
in the starlight. He would land
on a cloud and then climb up again.

One night he found a very long
moonbeam that went right down to earth.
Small Silver Bear went whizzing down.
It was the longest slide
that he had ever had.

" Take care," shouted the stars,
as he slid past them. But
Small Silver Bear laughed and whizzed
on till at last he came to the end.

He bounced on the roof of a house and
caught hold of a chimney pot.

He sat still for a minute till
he found out where he was.

That night it was very cold and
the big roof was white and shining.

Small Silver Bear touched the roof
with his paddy paw.
How slippery it was!
Just like ice and much better
than moonbeams for sliding down.

So Small Silver Bear slid down the
roofs all through the night.

He was so soft and bouncy that he did not hurt himself, even when he fell off the roof into the garden.

Then, just before morning, he climbed back up the moonbeam.
He curled up on a soft cloud beside the Moon and fell asleep.

Now that he had once tried sliding down the icy roofs Small Silver Bear was not happy with any other kind of sliding.

Every night he found a moonbeam on which to go to earth. He slid over the icy roof tops all night while people were asleep.

" Take care," cried the Moon ; " it's much better to play up here."

" Oh ! I shall come back safely," laughed Silver Bear.

He did, every time but one.

One night the Zoo Man was working
very late in his house.

He lived near the Zoo, and it was
his work to find new kinds of monkeys
and bears and elephants for the Zoo.

To-night he was reading about bears.
As he read, he found that the Zoo
had only very few kinds of bears.

There were many other kinds
in other lands over the seas.
He wished to find a new kind of bear.

He thought, " I will have my summer
holidays in a land far over the seas,
and look for a new bear."

Just then he looked up quickly,
and there was Small Silver Bear
sliding down the icy roof
of the house in front.
The Zoo Man rubbed his eyes.
THERE was a new kind of bear.

Just think of it : a new kind of bear—
a shining silver bear—in his own street!
What a surprise!

At that minute Small Silver Bear
climbed up a moonbeam and went
past him up to the Moon.

He curled himself up on a soft cloud
and went fast asleep.

The Zoo Man laughed and said
to himself, " I have thought so much
about bears that I am even dreaming
about them. It is very late ; I shall
go to bed."

But the next night
when he was working late
he saw Small Silver Bear again.
He saw him whizz down a moonbeam
on to the icy roof. He knew that
he had not been dreaming now.
He said, " I shall catch this bear
for the Zoo."

Quietly he took a ladder to the side
of the house.

He climbed up and went quietly
across the icy roof.

He caught hold of Small Silver Bear
before Small Silver Bear could think
what it was. Oh, what a surprise!

Now he was caught.

Poor little bear! He moved about
and kicked, but he couldn't get away.

Next day he was taken to the Zoo
and left by himself in a big wooden
cage. He was given some soft straw
on which to sleep.

The Zoo keepers were kind to him.
They gave him honey and bran to eat,
but Small Silver Bear didn't like it
very much.

His name was written on the cage.

People came to read it and
to look at this new kind of bear.

SMALL SILVER BEAR
WHO SLID FROM THE SKY

But Small Silver Bear curled up
under the straw and no one but
the keepers saw him. He was a very
unhappy Silver Bear.

Only at night he came out and then
he sat in a corner of the cage.
He was very sad and he longed for
his home with the Moon.

The Moon was sad and unhappy, too.
The moonbeams missed their friend
whizzing down on them to the earth.

The clouds missed Small Silver
Bear's bouncing, and the stars were
unhappy without him.

" Cheer up," said the Sun.
" I'll find him."

He shone brightly next day,
peeping in all the houses
and sending light
into the darkest places.

But the Sun could not find
Small Silver Bear anywhere.
He peeped in every dark corner.
Then he stopped shining brightly
and evening came on.

" We will look for him,"
cried the stars, and they twinkled
from behind the clouds that night.

But they could not find
Small Silver Bear anywhere.

" I shall search till morning," said
the Moon, and he tried so hard
that people on earth said,
" How bright it is to-night! "

And then a moonbeam found Small
Silver Bear. It shone right down on him
as he sat in the corner of his cage,
crying for his friend the Moon.

" Hullo," said Small Silver Bear,
and he began to climb up a moonbeam.

But when he had gone only a little way,
the bars at the top of the cage
stopped him.

He was too fat to push through
between the bars. He tugged at them,
but they were too strong to break.

" What can I do ? "
Small Silver Bear cried aloud.

Every night after that he sat
in the same corner of the cage
and the moonbeams came to talk to him.

But though he shook the gate
of the cage and pulled at the bars,
he could not get free.

" This little bear is growing thin,"
said the Zoo keepers ; " and in the
daytime he does not even look silver.
He just looks dirty white."

" I think he wants to be free,"
said the keeper who gave him his food
every day.

Then, because he was a kind keeper
and he liked the little bear,
he said to himself,
"I shall help Small Silver Bear."

So that evening he left the gate
of the cage unlocked.

Now the Sun saw that the gate was left
unlocked, and before he sank to rest
he told the first evening star.

The star told the Moon and
the moonbeam who came down to see
Small Silver Bear whispered to him,
"Your cage is unlocked."

Small Silver Bear pushed the gate.
It opened and he was free!

Quickly he ran to the moonbeam,
and in a minute he had climbed safely
up to the clouds. He curled up
and went fast asleep.

He never tried sliding over the roofs
again, however slippery they might look.
He slid only on the short moonbeams
which ended on the clouds.

"Where have you been all this time?"
asked one of the stars
who did not know.

Small Silver Bear looked surprised
and shook his head.

"I forget," he said, "but I know
I shall never go away again."

And he smiled at the Moon, curled
up on a cloud, and went to sleep again.

Exercises

DO YOU KNOW ?

The days of the week.

1. Sunday	5. Thursday
2. Monday	6. Friday
3. Tuesday	7. Saturday
4. Wednesday	

Which days do you go to school ?
Which days do you not go to school ?
Shops are closed all day on . . . . ?
Which day comes in the middle of the week ?

Do you know the months of the year ?

1. January	5. May	9. September
2. February	6. June	10. October
3. March	7. July	11. November
4. April	8. August	12. December

What is the name of the sixth month of the year ?
In which month is your birthday ?
In what months is the sun hot ?
What is the name of the third month of the year ?
In which month does Christmas Day come ?
Which months are very cold ?
In which months do the leaves fall off the trees ?

Puzzles

I am fat. My tail is curly. I like to roll in the mud. My nose is turned up at the end. I grunt. What am I ?

At first I am a very little egg. Then I become a grub and live on green leaves. Afterwards I change from a grub and I can fly about. I have pretty coloured wings. What am I now ?

When I am dug out of the ground I am rough and dirty. I am taken into a room and polished. I twinkle like the stars. I am made into rings and brooches. What am I ?

I go up and down. I carry people. I am found in some shops and tall buildings. I go from one floor to another. I can be made to go by just pressing a button. What am I ?

I live in North America. I have a brownish coloured skin. I sometimes wear feathers and live in a wigwam. I go hunting. Who am I ?

I am made of sticks and straw and old clothes. Sometimes I wear a hat and have a pipe in my mouth. I have an ugly face. Boys and girls make me. Sometimes they carry me about. I am burnt on November the fifth. What am I ?

I am round. I am made of silver or gold or copper or bronze. My name starts with *C*. What am I ?

Can You Guess?

chair	comb	clock

bottle	needle	shoe

1. Which has a tongue but cannot speak ?
2. Which has an eye but cannot see ?
3. Which has teeth but cannot bite ?
4. Which has legs but cannot walk ?
5. Which has a neck but cannot swallow ?
6. Which has hands but cannot hold anything in them ?

Who Knows?

1. What snow is made of ?
2. What sound a cat makes ?
3. What a baby dog is called ?
4. Where coal comes from ?
5. What butter is made from ?
6. Where you can buy meat ?
7. What lives in a stable ?
8. What the tyres of a car are made of ?
9. What day comes before Tuesday ?
10. What bird is black ?

Word List

This list contains the 383 new words used in Book 4 ; at this stage derivatives are not listed. The numbers refer to the pages on which the words first appear.

The list is useful for all pupils and is of particular benefit to slower readers who can be given confidence to start a new story by seeing, writing and tracing the new words beforehand. This method is explained in the *Happy Venture Teacher's Manual*.

1 holidays
seaside
cases

2 bucket
spade
clean
next
early

3 Mrs
Smith
while
ten
taxi

4 tickets
money
ask
half
returns
train
platform

5 signal
porter

6 know
count
raced

7 seven
where
turn

farm

8 soldiers
marching
grand
Duke
York
thousand
only
neither
nor

10 eight
twelve
glad
many

11 reached
won
quickly
gate
break

12 beach
great
shouted
sands
nice
castle
dig
yet

13 shells

wood
moat
fill

14 finished
breakfast
far
tide
wide
pools
fan
fish

15 sea-gull
why
oil
wings

16 ships
swims
towel
back
flew

17 hullo
someone
their
friend
Malcolm

18 to-night
before

19 Bombo

kind
more
than
twenty
years
long
trunk

20 named
Kip
worked
hard
woodyard
pile
logs

21 neck

22 rode
tailor's
twinkled
coat

23 bun
mouth

24 splashing
cool
squirted

25 always
pricked
end
pin

26 loud
started
angry
left
dirty

28 merry
new
penny

29 boat
music

30 circus
hay

31 should
pony
Tony

32 feed
seals
caught
dropped
flash
claps
flappers

33 stood
front

34 just
told
people
rows
done

35 clowns
fed
driven

36 chair
lady

37 stool
Jumbo
air

38 hear
tent
trumpet
drum
kept

39 slowly
passed
gone

40 swung
under
net
hung
clever

41 nasturtiums
proud
boots
raining
Roderick
also
begin

42 right
pretty
flowers
Ben
brought
holes
low

43 pair
ever
heels
falling
splitting
these

44 such

lay
weeks
often

45 himself
myself
street
spot

46 stones
picked
rich
soil

48 bought
seeds
plant
even
might

49 those
own

50 roof
cottage
spread
ourselves
gold
yellow
orange

51 above
shining

52 towards
butcher
shopkeeper

53 heard
wife
maids
parson

54 noise

55 burned
flames
doorstep
till
clothes

56 showed
climbed

58 thirsty
drink
better

59 warm
winter
summer
once
bright
knew

60 Joey
Kangaroo
Australia
strong
large
fur
pocket
lived
most

62 green
grass
dew
popped

63 every
smiled
wish
seek

64 place
resting

fence
dear
66 through
67 carry
bush
safe
69 race
71 lunch
picnic
cups
72 milk
bus
73 conductor
click
minutes
74 funnels
masts
75 watch
unloading
cranes
flour
wheat
wire
76 chains
77 painted
lands
port-holes
radio
78 gangway
officer
propellers
79 lifeboats

rock
81 tugs
82 drove
onwards
83 pointed
cliff
lighthouse
which
strike
84 flies
85 visit
87 boil
88 paper
laid
across
89 between
match
lit
camp
90 feel
hungry
91 move
frog
92 piece
seaweed
hang
dress
93 hunted
late
95 surprise
panda
together
96 turnstile

97 Ming
cage
paws
teddy
bear
herself
98 doesn't
Tang
99 chimpanzees'
101 led
102 spoons
Booboo
young
Jubilee
103 smack
beg
104 slid
television
forgotten
cloud
105 twiddled
paddy
curled
fond
stars
moonbeams
bounced
shone
106 earth
whizzing
care
past
107 touched
slippery

ice
108 soft
hurt
tried
109 few
rubbed
110 dreaming
111 quietly
poor
112 honey
bran
written
113 corner
missed
cheer
peeping
darkest
114 behind
search
115 bars
push
116 same
shook
thin
free
117 because
unlocked
sank
whispered
118 never
short

DARK
HORSES
JUMPS GUIDE 2017-2018

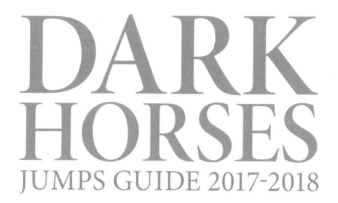

DARK
HORSES
JUMPS GUIDE 2017-2018

MARTEN JULIAN

Raceform

Published in 2017 by Raceform Ltd
27 Kingfisher Court, Hambridge Road, Newbury RG14 5SJ

Copyright © Marten Julian 2017

A catalogue record for this book is available from the British Library.

ISBN 978-1-910497-29-6

Designed by Neil Wadsworth

Printed and bound in the UK by Bishops Printers, Portsmouth, PO6 1TR

CONTENTS

INTRODUCTION	7
THE PREMIER HORSES	9
THE DARK HORSES	27
THE DARK HANDICAPPERS	65
THE POINT-TO-POINT RECRUITS	75
TAKING A LOOK BACK	117
THE 2018 CHAMPION HURDLE PREVIEW	121
THE 2018 CHELTENHAM GOLD CUP PREVIEW	135
INDEX	158

Keep in touch

If you want to keep in touch with Marten's thoughts on a regular basis then read his **free-to-view** journal at:

www.martenjulian.com

or ring him on

0906 150 1555

Selections given in first minute.
Calls charged at £1.50 a minute at all times

If you would like to avoid Premium Rate call charges please contact Rebecca on 01539 741 007 for details of our Telephone & Text Service.

Follow Marten
@martenjulian

Tel: 01539 741 007   Email: rebecca@martenjulian.com   www.martenjulian.com

INTRODUCTION

Thank you for buying this 2017-18 edition of the *Dark Horses Jumps Guide*. I hope that you find it a useful source of reference and enjoyment throughout the course of the season.

As always I am hopeful that the horses selected for the Premier List will yield a profit. It is my belief that they possess the specific attributes to warrant our special interest.

The Dark Horses section includes horses from a variety of backgrounds, notably a few recruits from France and the point-to-point field.

The Dark Handicappers section pinpoints a handful of horses that appear to be starting their campaigns from favourable marks.

My assistant Jodie Standing has been especially excited about the quality of recruits from the Irish point-to-point field this year so we make no apology for devoting a substantial amount of space to this year's feature.

I hope that you enjoy reading my previews of the Gold Cup and Champion Hurdle. As is often the case these days plans are very uncertain this far in advance, but I hope to have covered most of the eventualities.

As always I am indebted to my daughter Rebecca, Jodie Standing, Julian Brown, Ian Greensill, Neil Wadsworth and Paul Day for their guidance and contributions at various stages of the production.

If you wish to keep updated with my news and information about the featured horses then refer to my website www.martenjulian.com.

My weekly appraisals and assessments on the progress of the Premier List qualifiers, and other selected horses from the *Guide*, can be acquired through the *Weekend Card*.

Alternatively you can hear my views on a daily basis on 0906 150 1555, where any selections are given within the first minute of the message (calls charged at £1.50 a minute at all times). If you would like to avoid Premium Rate call charges please contact Rebecca on 01539 741 007 for details of our Telephone and Text Service.

If you wish to learn more about my services then refer to my website or contact Rebecca (rebecca@martenjulian.com).

Finally, I would like to wish you the very best of good fortune for the new season.

Bye for now

Marten

THE PREMIER HORSES

The following horses have been selected in the hope and expectation that they will reward support through the course of the season.

DEBECE (6YR BAY GELDING)

TRAINER:	**Tim Vaughan**
PEDIGREE:	**Kayf Tara – Dalamine (Sillery)**
HURDLE RATING:	**145**
FORM:	**441/123313 –**
OPTIMUM TRIP:	**2m 4f +**

Admirably consistent and talented young performer, with the tenacity to match his ability.

Looked a bit of a plodder in his first three starts in bumpers before easily winning at Market Rasen in March, 2016.

Made a successful hurdling debut at Kempton in May of that year, winning by eight lengths, before looking one-paced in his next three starts when second at Southwell, third at Cheltenham in his first handicap off 116 and third again off 120 at Aintree in December.

Showed much improved form next time at Newbury, lengthening in good style to beat Leaderofthedance by 19 lengths off 121.

Raised to 137 and ran a blinder on unfavourable terms stepped up to an extended three miles in the Grade 1 Doom Bar Sefton Novices' Hurdle, keeping on very gamely to run a half-length third to the 149-rated The Worlds End and Beyond Conceit.

Fifth foal and a three-parts brother to top-class performer Don Poli and a half-brother to other winners at up to two miles five furlongs.

Has been crying out for three miles and fences and looks a natural contender for the RSA Chase.

Rated very highly by his handler and has the class and potential to play a part in the top staying novice chase company this season. A very likeable sort.

JUST MINDED (6YR BAY GELDING)

TRAINER:	**Sue Smith**
PEDIGREE:	**Kayf Tara – Georgia On My Mind (Belmez)**
HURDLE RATING:	**122**
FORM:	**0/13312 –**
OPTIMUM TRIP:	**2m 4f +**

Attractive sort with scope, who confirmed the promise shown in his bumper debut at Market Rasen in April, 2016, when landing some decent bets to win at Carlisle in November. Responded well to strong pressure there to gradually get on top approaching the final furlong and win by four lengths.

Shaped well when third to Craggaknock over two miles on his hurdling debut at Wetherby in December but ran below that form next time over an extended 2m 4f at Ayr, making a few mistakes and one-paced in the closing stages.

Returned to winning ways two months later at Market Rasen in March, back down to an extended two miles and driven out to beat Top Ville Ben by three lengths. Ran well on his final start at Newcastle, finishing second to Ami Desbois over an extended 2m 4f at Newcastle.

Sue Smith – has a promising staying prospect with Just Minded

Fifth foal and a three-parts brother to the useful Diamond King, a winner up to 2m 5f, and Young Hurricane, a winner up to 3m 3f.

Caught the eye in the paddock when he won at Carlisle and impresses as the type to make into a long-distance handicap chaser in the north. A dour type, who is bred to stay well and built to jump a fence.

LASTBUTNOTLEAST (7YR CHESTNUT MARE)

TRAINER:	**Donald McCain**
PEDIGREE:	**Flemensfirth – Lakil Princess (Bering)**
HURDLE RATING:	**135**
FORM:	**P02110/111 –**
OPTIMUM TRIP:	**3m**

Took a while to get the message in point-to-points, not winning until her fourth run at Toomebridge in October, 2015.

Made all to beat three opponents in a modest bumper at Sedgefield in March, 2016, before finishing down the field behind Kayf Grace in the Grade 2 Mares' Open National Hunt Flat Race at Aintree in April.

Lastbutnotleast – did nothing but improve all season

Reappeared last December and looked a much-improved performer over hurdles, making all to beat Floramoss on her seasonal debut at Hexham. Again made all, stepped up to an extended 2m 3f, to beat Which One Is Which at Carlisle before showing the utmost tenacity to beat Happy Diva in a Listed contest over an extended three miles at Doncaster in March.

First foal of a mare that won over hurdles and fences from the family of 3m hurdle/chase winner Moskova.

Has shown both ability and courage in her races to date and is particularly well suited to testing ground. Looks an out-and-out galloper who will be at her best in midwinter conditions.

Has a most likeable way of galloping and has the talent to hold her own against the geldings.

LOUGH DERG SPIRIT (5YR BAY GELDING)

TRAINER:	**Nicky Henderson**
PEDIGREE:	**Westerner – Sno-Cat Lady (Executive Perk)**
HURDLE RATING:	**137**
FORM:	**3/1141P –**
OPTIMUM TRIP:	**2m +**

Warrants inclusion here on the strength of his exceptional hurdling.

Ran third on his point-to-point debut at Loughanmore in March, 2016, to the promising Claimantakinforgan, also now in this yard, before beating Minella Warrior at Athlacca in May.

Made his hurdling debut for this yard at Kempton in November, putting in an exceptionally slick round of jumping to beat Coup De Pinceau by three and a half lengths. Found it all too much for him when fourth of six to Capitaine in a Grade

Lough Derg Spirit – an outstanding jumper of a hurdle

2 contest at Ascot in December before returning to winning form when making all to beat Peter The Mayo Man with plenty in hand at Musselburgh in February.

Stepped back up in class to run in the Grade 1 Betway Mersey Novices' Hurdle at Aintree in April but lost his place half a mile from home and was pulled up after blundering at the second last.

Looks sure to make a useful novice chaser but trainer may try and exploit his mark over hurdles before then.

One of the slickest jumpers of a hurdle seen in the novice ranks for a long time.

MOUNT MEWS (6YR BAY GELDING)

TRAINER:	**Malcolm Jefferson**
PEDIGREE:	**Presenting – Kneeland Lass (Bob Back)**
HURDLE RATING:	**145**
FORM:	**1/112112 –**
OPTIMUM TRIP:	**2m 4f**

One of the most promising novice hurdlers in the north last season with the potential to progress further up the ladder.

Has yet to finish out of the first two in seven starts, winning both his bumpers at Market Rasen and Kelso in the spring of 2016. Made a winning hurdling debut at Kelso in December before meeting his first defeat when caught in the last couple of strides by Eaton Hill at Wetherby in January.

Returned to winning ways at Doncaster 13 days later before landing a Grade 2 contest by 49 lengths at Kelso in March. Showed courage to finish second on his final start in the Grade 1 Crabbie's Top Novices' Hurdle at Aintree despite never travelling that well and looking held turning for home.

Second foal of a modest but well-related full sister to top staying chaser Burton Port from the family of Blazing Walker.

Rated by his handler as good a young horse as he's had. Expected to continue over hurdles for the time being with the option of switching to fences in the new year.

Mount Mews – has plenty more to offer

Only does the minimum required to win but finds plenty if required and has a good attitude. May prove best suited to a strongly run two miles at this stage of his career. Has plenty more still to offer.

NOT THAT FUISSE (4YR BAY GELDING)

TRAINER:	**Dan Skelton**
PEDIGREE:	**Fuisse – Edelmira (Kahyasi)**
FORM:	**1 -**
OPTIMUM TRIP:	**2m**

One of the most impressive, if not the most impressive, winners of a bumper seen anywhere last season.

Made his debut in a Class 6 contest at Warwick, held up in arrears before swinging into contention from the turn for home. Pulling double when allowed to take the lead and produced an instant change of gear to beat the promising Quick Pick with plenty in hand by four lengths.

Second foal and a full brother to 2m hurdle winner Peruvien Bleu out of a half-sister to French 2m 3f hurdle/chase winner Square Ortoloan.

Form later upheld by third Equus Amadeus, who won his next two races.

Dan Skelton – now a friendly rival to his former boss

One of many promising young horses from a strong stable but likely to prove a serious player if he takes to hurdles. Has a potent turn of foot and is one to keep a very close eye on.

POTTERMAN (4YR BAY GELDING)

TRAINER:	**Alan King**
PEDIGREE:	**Sulamani – Polly Potter (Kayf Tara)**
FORM:	**1**
OPTIMUM TRIP:	**2m 4f**

A risky inclusion on the slim evidence to hand, but left a strong impression with the manner of his victory especially given the depth of stamina in his pedigree.

Made his debut in a low-grade bumper event at Huntingdon in May, starting 13/8 to beat five rivals. Travelling well just off the pace, he made very smooth headway to move alongside the leader in the straight before quickening in a few strides to shoot clear and win hard held by ten lengths.

Form nothing to write home about, but displayed an awesome turn of foot for a horse bred to stay so well.

Second foal of a full sister to useful bumper/hurdle winner Kayf Grace from the family of the top-class chaser Denman.

Expected to take high rank in novice hurdles with the potential to flourish when stepped up to two and a half miles.

RAVENHILL ROAD (6YR CHESTNUT GELDING)

TRAINER:	Brian Ellison
PEDIGREE:	Exit To Nowhere – Zaffarella (Zaffaran)
FORM:	111 -
OPTIMUM TRIP:	2m +

One of the most exciting young prospects in the north and confidently expected to make the grade in novice hurdles.

Purchased by these connections for £100,000 in May, 2016, after beating subsequent winner Stingthebookies by 15 lengths at Broughshane in May.

Made his debut for this stable in a bumper at Market Rasen in October, making all before being headed leaving the back straight and then regaining the lead and responding well to driving to power away from the home turn. Looked very inexperienced in the straight, lugging left throughout, but still able to beat the runner-up by 14 lengths.

Ridden with more restraint next time at Doncaster, tracking the leaders before being allowed to ease ahead a furlong out. Still showed signs of greenness but kept on well to beat Molly Childers and subsequent dual-hurdle winner Take To Heart eased down in the closing stages.

First foal of a daughter of a mare that won over hurdles at distances up to two miles seven furlongs.

Has a long loping stride at the gallop and moves effortlessly through a race. Shapes as if he will appreciate two and a half miles in time, but has sufficient pace to win races at two.

There is a slight concern about his tendency to hang in the closing stages, but has talent to burn and could conceivably have the class to make an impression in the south.

SAM BROWN (5YR BAY GELDING)

TRAINER:	Anthony Honeyball
PEDIGREE:	Black Sam Bellamy – Cream Cracker (Sir Harry Lewis)
FORM:	11 -
OPTIMUM TRIP:	2m 4f +

Already appeals as a possible contender for the Neptune Novices' Hurdle at Cheltenham in March.

Displayed a tremendous attitude when responding to pressure from some way out to beat Lalor by one and a quarter lengths in a bumper run in heavy ground at Wincanton in February having looked beaten at many stages of the race.

Defied a 7lb penalty next time at Newbury, travelling better on this occasion and finding a turn of foot to beat Chef Des Obeaux by three-quarters of a length.

Form could hardly have worked out better, with Lalor – already a winner at Wincanton on Boxing Day – winning his next two races including the Grade 2 contest at Aintree in April. Talkischeap, third at Newbury, won two bumpers at the end of the season.

Not especially well bred – out of a 2m hurdle/chase winning sister to a bumper winner – but has to rank as one of the best bumper performers of last season with a tenacity to match.

An exciting prospect for novice hurdles, especially when asked to stretch beyond two miles.

SAMCRO (5YR CHESTNUT GELDING)

TRAINER:	**Gordon Elliott**
PEDIGREE:	**Germany – Dun Dun (Saddlers' Hall)**
FORM:	**1/111 -**
OPTIMUM TRIP:	**2m 4f**

Beat the useful Elegant Escape, who is now with Colin Tizzard and rated on 137, by a length in his point-to-point at Monksgrange in April, 2016.

Stayed on well to make a successful bumper debut at a fog-cloaked Punchestown in November and then all out to hold Good Thyne Tara by half a length in a Listed bumper at Navan in December.

Put up his most impressive display on his last appearance at Fairyhouse in April, quickening to pull well clear of Cluan Dara by 17 lengths.

Bought for £335,000 after winning his point-to-point, he is the fourth foal half-brother to Cocacobana, a winner at up to three miles, out of an unraced sister to 2m to 3m 1f hurdle/chase winner Master Of The Hall and the useful Featherbed Lane, from the family of top-class jumper Sound Man.

Very highly rated by his handler, who has as good a line to bumper form as anyone. Bred to stay well and expected to figure at the top level in novice hurdles, with the Neptune Novices' Hurdle in March a possible long-term objective.

TEA FOR TWO (8YR BAY GELDING)

TRAINER:	**Nick Williams**
PEDIGREE:	**Kayf Tara – One For Me (Tragic Role)**
CHASE RATING:	**164**
FORM:	**1/221/13112P/00113/0241U1 –**
OPTIMUM TRIP:	**3m +**

Would not seem an obvious inclusion for this section, having raced for five seasons, but is now rated on his highest ever mark and has the potential to improve yet further.

Was a fair hurdler, notably striding away to win the 2015 Lanzarote Hurdle by 16 lengths from a mark of 134. Failed to trouble the judge in four subsequent starts but made an immediate impression when switched to chasing in December of that year, winning a 2m 3f novices' chase at Exeter by ten lengths and then beating Southfield Royale by four lengths in the 3m Grade 1 Kauto Star Novices' Chase at Kempton on Boxing Day. Far from disgraced dropped back to 2m 4f when third to Bristol De Mai in the Scilly Isles Novices' Chase at Sandown, typically keeping on well in the closing stages.

Shaped adequately on first two starts back last autumn, notably when second to Josses Hill in the 2m 4f Peterborough Chase at Huntingdon, before running his best race up to that time when a gallant fourth to Thistlecrack, beaten three and a half lengths, in the King George VI Chase at Kempton.

Beat Henri Parry Morgan by 17 lengths next time at Exeter before blundering badly and unseating his rider at the second fence in the Gold Cup. Made amends on his next start in the 3m 1f Grade 1 Betway Bowl Chase at Aintree, keeping on strongly to beat Cue Card by a neck, with Smad Place a further 15 lengths back in third.

Tea For Two – returning triumphant

Was thought to favour a right-handed track until running so well at Aintree. Does dressage at home to keep him fresh and may still have improvement to come, having run just nine times over fences.

Lines from his Kempton and Aintree form suggest he would not have been far away in the Gold Cup but for his early misfortune. Has every right to serious consideration for this season's top honours especially given the improvement he showed for the step up to 3m 1f at Aintree. Bred to relish the extra distance of the Gold Cup and goes particularly well for Lizzie Kelly.

Would not be available at 50/1 for the Gold Cup if he came from a higher-profile yard. Has to be rated a serious contender on the evidence to hand.

WAITING PATIENTLY (6YR BAY GELDING)

TRAINER:	**Malcolm Jefferson**
PEDIGREE:	**Flemensfirth – Rossavon (Beneficial)**
CHASE RATING:	**150**
FORM:	**221/111 –**
OPTIMUM TRIP:	**2m 4f**

One of the most progressive and consistent young chasers in the north, with the potential to prove superior to handicap class.

Shaped very well in the 2015/16 season for former handler Keith Reveley, running Cloudy Dream to one and a quarter lengths on his second start in an extended 2m 3f novices' hurdle at Doncaster, before winning a 2m 4f novices' hurdle at Sedgefield in January.

Moved to this trainer on the retirement of his former handler and made a winning debut over fences from a mark of 123 in an extended 2m novices' handicap chase at Sedgefield in November, winning with more in hand than the seven lengths margin would suggest.

Beat Forest Bihan a few days later over the same trip at Newcastle before handling a step up in class to beat the useful Politologue by one and a quarter lengths in a 2m 4f Grade 2 novices' chase at Haydock.

Second foal of an unraced half-sister to 2m 4f hurdle/chase winner Ciara's Prince, 3m hurdle/chase winner Jo Jo Boy and 3m 1f hurdle/chase winner Yankee Jamie.

Both trainer and owner have stressed that they were not going to ask too much of the horse last season in the belief that he would reward patient handling.

A careful rather than spectacular jumper, he travels well through a race and relishes soft ground. Bred to stay three miles in time and has the ability to win again off 150 before stepping up in grade.

Malcolm Jefferson – has one of his strongest teams for the new campaign

THE DARK HORSES

The following horses are thought to have the potential to win races or improve further on their performances to date. They are drawn from a variety of backgrounds and should be noted with the long term in mind.

AIR NAVIGATOR (6YR BAY GELDING)

TRAINER:	Tom George
PEDIGREE:	Yeats – Lox Lane (Presenting)
FORM:	1 -
OPTIMUM TRIP:	2m +

Hard to assess on the evidence of his sole start last season, but travelled very smoothly into the race before displaying signs of greenness inside the final furlong.

Tom George – assessing the scene

Made his debut at Exeter in February, beating Harefield by one and a quarter lengths. Form of the race subsequently shown to be moderate, but won in the style of a useful horse.

Fifth foal out of an unraced half-sister to 3m hurdle/chase winner Duncliffe and 2m 6f hurdle winner Melba Toast from the family of the top-class performer Dramatist.

An imposing sort with the scope to improve. Will stay well.

ANNAMIX (4YR BAY GELDING)

TRAINER:	**Willie Mullins**
PEDIGREE:	**Martaline – Tashtiyana (Doyoun)**
FORM:	**2 -**
OPTIMUM TRIP:	**2m**

Ran second in a 2m hurdle contest in France for Guillaume Macaire.

Dam ran just once, unplaced on the Flat, but has proved very successful at stud, with four individual winners on the Flat including the very useful Tashkani and two over jumps.

Bred from one of the Aga Khan's highly successful bloodlines and is apparently shaping up well for his new connections.

ANTEY (4YR BAY GELDING)

TRAINER:	**Willie Mullins**
PEDIGREE:	**Lord Of England – Achinora (Sleeping Indian)**
FORM:	**13 -**
OPTIMUM TRIP:	**2m +**

Won an extended 1m 5f maiden in the French Provinces in July, 2016. Third on his next start over a slightly shorter trip.

Subsequently acquired in November by these connections for €130,000. First foal out of a German 1m winner who is a half-sister to a useful winner up to two miles.

Shapes as if he may need a trip.

BETTER GETALONG (6YR BAY GELDING)

TRAINER:	Nicky Richards
PEDIGREE:	Gold Well – Arequipa (Turtle Island)
FORM:	2/110 -
OPTIMUM TRIP:	2m 4f

A very promising prospect for novice hurdles.

Shaped well in bumpers, running second to Westend Story at Huntingdon in December, 2015, on his sole start of the 2015/16 campaign.

Reappeared just under a year later, beating the useful Sam's Adventure by a short head at Ayr having come on and off the bridle for the last mile of the race. Again made hard work of landing odds of 1/4 next time at Kelso before travelling south to Cheltenham for the Weatherbys Champion Bumper.

Shaped better than his finishing position suggests, missing the break causing him to lose early ground on the main pack. Travelled well in arrears before making steady progress on the outside from the second last turn, looming up as the field turned for home before struggling with the quickening pace. Still within ten lengths or so of the leaders approaching the final furlong and kept on steadily thereafter to finish 12th of 22, fourteen and a half lengths behind the winner.

First foal of an Irish point-to-point winner from the successful family of Mossy Fern, One Sniff and Coq Hardi Affair.

Tends to get outpaced but nothing wrong with his attitude and looks sure to benefit from hurdles and a step up beyond two miles. One to keep in mind for the longer term, especially when he is sent chasing.

BIG RIVER (7YR BAY GELDING)

TRAINER:	**Lucinda Russell**
PEDIGREE:	**Milan – Call Kate (Lord Americo)**
HURDLE RATING:	**144**
FORM:	**221/1/21021 –**
OPTIMUM TRIP:	**3m +**

Consistent and progressive sort, with a future over fences assuming he does not spend the season in handicap hurdles.

Bought for £50,000 in December, 2014, a month after running a good second at Glenbane in his sole start between the flags. Looked highly promising in his bumpers, running second to the high-class Brain Power at Newcastle in February and then beating Gully's Edge by a head at Kelso in March.

Won a maiden hurdle back at Kelso in October, 2015, but then absent until the following October when running second from a mark of 115 in a 2m 0-115 handicap hurdle. Hacked up on the bridle next time at Ayr, tongue-tied for the first time, over an extended 2m 5f from a mark of 115 before finding the track too sharp when fifth of ten to Clondaw Kaempfer in a 3m 0-140 at Musselburgh.

Second next time at Haydock to the very useful Dadsintrouble, trying to concede the winner 2lb, before improving again to beat Seeyouatmidnight from a mark of

Milan – in full flight

132 over 3m 2f at Kelso in March.

Improved by an official margin of 29lb last season clearly benefiting from the application of a tongue-tie and the step up in trip. Has the look of a potential Grand National contender.

Likely to be sent novice chasing this season but one to note for the long term as well. Loves soft ground and a test of stamina.

BULLIONAIRE (4YR BAY GELDING)

TRAINER:	**Harry Fry**
PEDIGREE:	**Gold Well – Dontcallerthat (Anshan)**
FORM:	**1 -**
OPTIMUM TRIP:	**2m +**

Extremely promising son of Gold Well, who beat 19 rivals in a useful bumper with complete authority.

Made his debut in a Newbury bumper in March, racing handily until taking up the running on reaching the straight and striding out confidently to beat Midnight Stroll by three and a half lengths. Form has held up quite well, with the fifth winning on his hurdling debut this autumn.

First foal of a modest point-to-point winning half-sister to 3m 2f hunter chase winner Monty's Lass.

Likely to be brought along quietly by his patient handler. Much to like about the way he went about his business at Newbury and not hard to see him becoming a top novice over hurdles.

BURROWS SAINT (4YR BAY GELDING)

TRAINER:	**Willie Mullins**
PEDIGREE:	**Saint Des Saints – La Bombonera (Mansonnien)**
FORM:	**02/042 -**
OPTIMUM TRIP:	**2m +**

Raced five times in France as a three-year-old, three times over hurdles and twice over fences.

Ran second to the subsequently useful Flying Tiger – now rated 141 over hurdles in the UK – on the second of his three outings in April, 2016. Shaped well when fourth and second in two starts over fences, both times on testing ground.

Shares the same sire as stable companion Djakadam and expected to prove a decent staying novice chaser.

CAPTAIN MCGARRY (5YR BAY GELDING)

TRAINER:	Graeme Mcpherson
PEDIGREE:	Oscar – Garryduff Princess (Husyan)
FORM:	1 -
OPTIMUM TRIP:	2m 4f +

Surprised his trainer when proving sharp enough to beat 13 rivals in a bumper at Kempton in March.

Always handy, moved into second turning for home and went into the lead holding on to win by four lengths from Colonial Dreams despite drifting left in the closing stages.

Form subsequently upheld by runner-up, who won a bumper at Southwell by 26 lengths just over a month later.

Seventh foal and a half-brother to 3m 1f hurdle/chase winner Court By Surprise and 3m hurdle/chase winner Drive On Jim. Dam is a half-sister to bumper and 3m hurdle winner Garryduff Supreme.

Did well to win a bumper given the stamina in his pedigree. Has been given time to find his way and will probably prove useful, especially when asked to tackle a distance of ground.

Graeme McPherson – has a nice prospect on his hands

CATWELLS (4YR BLACK GELDING)

TRAINER:	Willie Mullins
PEDIGREE:	Irish Wells – Cathelie (Sleeping Car)
FORM:	1/
OPTIMUM TRIP:	2m

Ran well to win his sole start in France, beating subsequent triple-winner Monsieur Co – now with Paul Nicholls – by five lengths at Nancy in April, 2016.

Missed last season through injury and may not be easy to place, but no doubting his talent and could prove effective in novice chases.

CHACUN POUR SOI (5YR BAY GELDING)

TRAINER:	Willie Mullins
PEDIGREE:	Policy Maker – Kruscyna (Ultimately Lucky)
FORM:	1203/
OPTIMUM TRIP:	2m +

Ran three times over hurdles, winning on his debut at Dieppe in August, 2015, and running fifth of 13 in a Listed race at Auteuil in November. Returned for his chase debut at Enghien in March, 2016, finishing third of seven beaten two lengths by King's Socks, now with David Pipe and rated 147.

Clearly useful and expected to go directly chasing.

CHAMP (5YR BAY GELDING)

TRAINER:	Nicky Henderson
PEDIGREE:	King's Theatre – China Sky (Definite Article)
FORM:	12 -
OPTIMUM TRIP:	2m

Made his debut in a Class 6 bumper at Southwell in January, heavily supported to 8/15 and travelling well throughout before drawing away to beat Grey Warbler by three and a half lengths.

Again made odds-on to defy a penalty the following month at Kempton but beaten two and a quarter lengths by well-regarded Doncaster bumper winner Irish Prophecy.

First foal of a half-sister to triple Gold Cup winner Best Mate, the useful staying hurdler/chaser Cornish Rebel and the talented Inca Trail, a winner up to three and a half miles.

Has a strong predisposition to good ground on both sides of his pedigree. Very well regarded and expected to prove one of the yard's better novice hurdlers.

CLAIMANTAKINFORGAN (5YR BAY GELDING)

TRAINER:	Nicky Henderson
PEDIGREE:	Great Pretender – Taquine D'Estrees (Take Risks)
FORM:	S1/10235 -
OPTIMUM TRIP:	2m +

Stayed on well to win a point-to-point at Loughanmore from Kildisart and Lough Derg Spirit – also now in this yard – in March, 2016.

Sold for £110,000 a month later and had his first run for new connections at Haydock in November, winning a bumper by one and three-quarter lengths from Global Stage. Sixth in a Listed bumper at Ascot just less than a month later then second to Black Op in a Doncaster bumper in February.

Showed much improved form next time, when finishing strongly into third behind Fayonagh in the Weatherbys Champion Bumper at Cheltenham. Possibly ran a little below that level next time, when fifth of 19 to Lalor in the Grade 2 National Hunt Flat Race at Aintree.

Ended the season one of the top half-dozen bumper horses in the UK. Has all the attributes required to become a top-flight novice hurdler.

DAME DE COMPAGNIE (4YR BAY FILLY)

TRAINER:	**Nicky Henderson**
PEDIGREE:	**Lucarno – Programmee (Kahyasi)**
FORM:	**22 -**
OPTIMUM TRIP:	**2m**

Shaped with great promise in her two starts in France, running Drive Again to two lengths in a 1m 4f AQPS Flat race at Craon in September, 2016, before finishing second to Duca De Thaix in a 2m 2f conditions hurdle at Auteuil in October. The winner has since been bought by Gigginstown Stud to run from Gordon Elliott's yard.

Fourth foal and a half-sister to Flat/chase winner Belle Affaire and Vie Sa Vie, winner of a 2m 2f hurdle. Dam won a 2m 2f chase and is a half-sister to useful performers Hard Rock, Sortie De Secours and Un Jour Ou L'Autre.

Has delighted her trainer since moving to Seven Barrows and expected to take full advantage of the mares' programme.

DAPHNE DU CLOS (4YR BAY FILLY)

TRAINER:	Nicky Henderson
PEDIGREE:	Spanish Moon – Katarina Du Clos (Panoramic)
FORM:	121 -
OPTIMUM TRIP:	2m

Confidently expected to take high rank as a hurdler, having impressed with the style of her victory in a Listed bumper at Newbury in February.

Ran once in France, beating 11 rivals in a 1m 4f AQPS bumper at Saint-Brieuc in October, 2016. Beaten a head on her UK debut in a 1m 6f bumper at Cheltenham in January,

Nicky Henderson – another very strong team of young talent

hampered close home, before stepping up to an extended two miles for a Listed event at Newbury.

Travelled sweetly throughout and moved upsides to challenge the leaders two furlongs from home, effortlessly taking the lead before quickening instantly to go clear of the gallant Western Ryder, who was conceding 21lb.

Form looks gilt-edged, with runner-up and third running virtually to the pound next time when fifth and sixth to Fayonagh in the Weatherbys Champion Bumper at Cheltenham, with the third later winning a bumper at Ludlow.

This is probably the best bumper form outside the spring festivals. A high-class filly with a turn of foot, who may be saved for the Cheltenham bumper in March.

DELIRANT (4YR BAY GELDING)

TRAINER:	David Pipe
PEDIGREE:	Khalkevi – Kusea (Useful)
FORM:	11 -
OPTIMUM TRIP:	2m +

Unraced in this country for owner JP McManus but a winner of both his starts in bumpers in France, beating Deesse Mome by five lengths at Pornichet-La Baule in October, 2016, and then beating Divine Sainte by four lengths at Saint-Cloud in November.

Raced keenly both times but won eased down on the second occasion and clearly a useful young horse.

Likely to make an impression in novice hurdles but needs to learn to relax.

DEMOPOLIS (3YR BAY GELDING)

TRAINER:	**Philip Hobbs**
PEDIGREE:	**Poliglote – Princess Demut (Tannenkonig)**
FORM:	**1**
OPTIMUM TRIP:	**2m**

Owned by JP McManus and the winner of his sole start in France, landing a 1m 7f conditions hurdle in May by a neck from Shark Du Berlais and Enfant Du Pays, who both ran well in their subsequent races.

Has a similar profile to other juvenile hurdlers that have done well for this yard and described as a lovely prospect by his trainer.

DIVA RECONCE (4YR BAY FILLY)

TRAINER:	**Kim Bailey**
PEDIGREE:	**Kap Rock – Kruscyna (Ultimately Lucky)**
FORM:	**1 -**
OPTIMUM TRIP:	**2m**

Intriguing once-raced filly who overcame extreme signs of greenness to beat seven rivals in a Warwick bumper in February.

Well supported beforehand, came on and off the bridle throughout the race, struggling to handle the turns, but came upsides ears pricked on turning into the straight and went away to win by seven lengths despite wandering both left and right.

Second foal and a half-sister to a French 2m 1f hurdle winner from a good family on the dam's side.

Will be an interesting recruit to hurdling provided she has learned from her experience at Warwick.

DOSTAL PHIL (4YR BAY GELDING)

TRAINER:	**Philip Hobbs**
PEDIGREE:	**Coastal Path – Quiphile (Panoramic)**
FORM:	**1 -**
OPTIMUM TRIP:	**2m**

Won an AQPS Flat race over an extended 1m 4f at Deauville in October, 2016 by a length and a quarter from Demon D'Aunou. Was bought by these connections two months later for €295,000 at the Arqana Autumn Sale.

Has pleased his trainer in the little he has done and expected to have a part to play in the novice hurdle ranks.

DU SOLEIL (5YR CHESTNUT GELDING)

TRAINER:	**Venetia Williams**
PEDIGREE:	**Zambezi Sun – Cykapri (Cyborg)**
FORM:	**1/3 -**
OPTIMUM TRIP:	**2m 4f +**

One of the nicest young prospects in this yard.

Hacked up on his racecourse debut in a Haydock bumper in November, 2015, travelling smoothly on the bridle and then quickening away to win comfortably by six lengths.

Off the track until last January and shaped with eye-catching promise in a 2m maiden hurdle at Chepstow. Held up off the pace, he made steady late headway to finish third having never been near enough to mount a challenge.

Half-brother to a hurdle/chase winner in France out of a sister to 2m 5f winner Cyborsun from the family of Geos and Kapgarde.

Venetia Williams – the trainer of Du Soleil

Sure to have derived great benefit from his run and remains a novice for the new season.

Evidently not been easy to train, given his lengthy absence from the track, but will be allowed all the time he needs to realise his potential by his gifted and most patient of handlers.

EPICURIS (5YR BAY GELDING)

TRAINER:	**Willie Mullins**
PEDIGREE:	**Rail Link – Argumentative (Observatory)**
FORM:	**111/204/20 -**
OPTIMUM TRIP:	**2m**

Very useful performer in France when trained by Criquette Head-Maarek, winning all three starts at two including a

Group 3 at Longchamp and the 1m 2f Group 1 Criterium de Saint-Cloud, making all to beat Palang by two and a half lengths.

Ran second in a 1m 2f Group 3 in April, 2015, and then far from disgraced when fifth to Golden Horn in the 2015 Derby. Best subsequent run was when runner-up to Sussudio in a Listed race at Maisons-Laffitte in April, 2016. Not been seen on the track since May, 2016.

Grew to dislike the starting stalls but has been sweetened up by his new connections and only needs to reproduce a fraction of his earlier form to make an impression over jumps.

A very interesting prospect.

FORGOT TO ASK (5YR BAY GELDING)

TRAINER:	**Tom George**
PEDIGREE:	**Ask – Lady Transcend (Aristocracy)**
FORM:	**F221 -**
OPTIMUM TRIP:	**2m 4f +**

Shaped well in point-to-points, running second at Dromahane last November and then again when second to Rambling Rector a fortnight later at Mainstown.

Subsequently purchased by this trainer for £35,000 and looked well bought when beating Battle Of Ideas very comfortably by 11 lengths in a Chepstow bumper in April.

Second foal of a point-to-point winning mare who is a full sister to useful staying chaser Lord Transcend and a chase winner over 2m 6f.

Well related and clearly talented. Looks a natural for staying novice hurdles before switching to fences in a year's time.

GREY MIST (3YR GREY GELDING)

TRAINER:	Tim Easterby
PEDIGREE:	Mastercraftsman – Kekova (Montjeu)
FORM (FLAT):	030000
OPTIMUM TRIP:	2m

Very lazy horse who shaped with a modicum of promise in three maiden races before switching to handicaps, finishing down the field over 1m 6f off marks of 65 and twice off 62.

Third foal of a French middle-distance winning half-sister to Listed-placed Casilda from the family of High Chaparral and Arc third Kozana.

Bred to improve for a step up in trip. Ideal sort for juvenile novice hurdling.

GUMBALL (3YR GREY GELDING)

TRAINER:	Philip Hobbs
PEDIGREE:	No Risk At All – Good Time Girl (Slickly)
FORM:	3 - 1
OPTIMUM TRIP:	2m +

Caught the eye on his first start, outpaced in arrears before staying on steadily in the straight, to finish a never-nearer third to Sharock in a 2m hurdle in Dieppe. Jumped quite well throughout and not given a hard time at any stage of the race.

Confirmed that promise when winning a Class 4 hurdle very easily at Stratford this October.

Dam placed twice on the Flat in France over seven furlongs. Sire a dual 1m Listed winner at two and twice a 1m 2f Listed winner at four.

Expected to prove far superior to the run-of-the-mill early-season novice hurdler. Jumps well and can quicken.

JERRYSBACK (5YR BAY GELDING)

TRAINER:	**Philip Hobbs**
PEDIGREE:	**Jeremy – Get A Few Bob Back (Bob Back)**
HURDLE RATING:	**139**
FORM:	**42/F111 -**
OPTIMUM TRIP:	**2m +**

One of last season's most promising novice hurdlers but was deliberately put away in March to allow him time to develop.

Did not appear to be anything special in Irish point-to-points, finishing fourth, second and then falling on his first three starts. Won at Loughanmore at his fourth attempt in October, 2016, but then made an immediate impression on his first start for these connections when winning an extended 2m 4f novices' hurdle at Plumpton in January hard on the bridle.

Reappeared just under a month later and beat Plus One in an extended 2m 3f novices' hurdle at Wetherby, again winning hard held.

Could be very well treated on 139 given the ease with which he won, but reported more likely to go directly over fences.

May reward connections for resisting the temptation to go to Cheltenham. Could be anything.

JET SET (5YR BAY MARE)

TRAINER:	Charlie Longsdon
PEDIGREE:	Getaway – Lavender Track (Pistolet Bleu)
FORM:	1 -
OPTIMUM TRIP:	2m 4f +

Winner of a point-to-point by five lengths from Kilnesare Kate at Dromahane in April and subsequently sold at Goffs for €80,000.

Third foal of a bumper and 2m 3f hurdle winner from the family of useful 2m 6f chase/hurdle winner Make A Track and the useful staying chaser Irish Cavalier, from the family of Champion Hurdle winner Make A Stand.

Always travelled well in her point-to-point, despite the odd mistake, and has impressed those who have ridden her at home.

Shows enough to suggest she could warrant a run in a Listed bumper. One to keep on your side.

JUGE ET PARTI (4YR GREY GELDING)

TRAINER:	Christian Williams
PEDIGREE:	Martaline – Nakota Rag (Nikos)
FORM:	1 -
OPTIMUM TRIP:	2m +

Made a strong impression when displaying a potent turn of foot to beat Asking Questions by 15 lengths in a Bangor bumper in April on his sole start.

Third there, a neck behind the runner-up, progressed to win a bumper at Carlisle next time out.

Fifth foal and a half-brother to a French hurdle winner out of a mare from the family of the useful Royal Rosa.

Hard to assess on the basis of one run, but evidently has ability and his turn of foot could prove an invaluable weapon.

JUST YOUR TYPE (5YR BROWN GELDING)

TRAINER:	**Charlie Longsdon**
PEDIGREE:	**Morozov – Enistar (Synefos)**
FORM:	**1 -**
OPTIMUM TRIP:	**2m 4f +**

Stands 18 hands and the winner of a 3m point-to-point at Lismore in March, overcoming a handful of sloppy jumps before beating Oscar Nomination by half a length having looked held jumping the last. Mixed messages from the form, with the fourth winning next time out.

Third foal of an unraced half-sister to useful hurdler and chaser Boychuk and Golden Chieftain, so bred to stay very well.

Bought for £40,000 at Cheltenham in March, 11 days after his success.

Won his point-to-point in heavy ground, so likely to come into his own when stamina is at a premium. One for the longer term.

LAD OF LUCK (4YR BAY GELDING)

TRAINER:	Jonjo O'Neill
PEDIGREE:	Soldier Of Fortune – Baraka Du Berlais (Bonnet Rouge)
FORM:	1 -
OPTIMUM TRIP:	2m

Hard to assess on the basis of his one run in a Chepstow bumper in February, but could not have left a better impression and in the right hands to thrive in his novice season over hurdles.

Made smooth progress from mid-division before responding immediately when asked to quicken and beat the runner-up Hidden Impact by 11 lengths, with a subsequent winner three-quarters of a length further back in third.

Third foal and a half-brother to the very promising hurdle winner Let's Dance. The dam, a winner of a chase and Listed hurdle, is a half-sister to 2m 4f winner Bacchus Du Berlais.

Has a turn of foot, on the evidence of his sole start, and bred to stay beyond two miles in time.

LISDOONVARNA LAD (5YR BAY GELDING)

TRAINER:	Charlie Longsdon
PEDIGREE:	Westerner – Socialite Girl (Glacial Storm)
FORM:	Unraced
OPTIMUM TRIP:	2m 4f +

Good-looking horse purchased privately from Ireland and a half-brother to All Downhill, who was placed in a bumper, and point-to-point winner Llangwm Lad. Half-brother to same stable's Stormy Milan.

Comes from the family of Express Leader and top-class chaser Buck House.

Rangy sort with the potential to develop into a useful staying chaser in time. Likely to need two and a half miles to be seen at his best over hurdles.

MAHARI (4YR BAY GELDING)

TRAINER:	Kerry Lee
PEDIGREE:	Duke Of Marmalade – Mission Secrete (Galileo)
FORM:	01/11130 -
OPTIMUM TRIP:	2m

Highly regarded ex-French import and winner of four races on the Flat, once over 1m 2f as a two-year-old and three more in 2016 at trips ranging from 1m 2f to 1m 4f.

Was subsequently raised in class and ran third of five to Talismanic in a 1m 4f Listed contest at Saint-Cloud before not being disgraced when last of five in a Group 3 contest at Chantilly in June.

Made his debut for these connections in a Class 4 novices' hurdle at Aintree in May, taking a keen hold and losing his place half a mile from home and being pulled up (broke a blood vessel).

Remains a novice for this season and clearly has the class to do well if he takes to hurdles.

MON PORT (5YR BAY GELDING)

TRAINER:	Olly Murphy
PEDIGREE:	Scorpion – Sounds Charming (Presenting)
FORM:	402 - 1
OPTIMUM TRIP:	2m +

Formerly with Ben De Haan and shaped well in bumpers, running a neck second to Dans Le Vent at Ludlow in April on his third outing.

Displayed vast improvement the following month at Warwick, starting at 2/5 and making all to beat Nuclear by 55 lengths.

Fourth foal of an unraced half-sister to staying hurdle/chase winner The Reverend from the family of Champion Hurdle runner-up Classical Charm.

Trainer, who has made such a good start to his career, has singled this one out for special mention.

MONTY'S AWARD (5YR BAY GELDING)

TRAINER:	Charlie Longsdon
PEDIGREE:	Oscar - Montys Miss (Presenting)
FORM:	14 -
OPTIMUM TRIP:	2m 4f +

Stayed on well to land some bets at long odds in a Worcester bumper in October, beating Eskendash – a winner over a 1m 3f maiden on the Flat and now rated on 77 – and subsequent hurdle winner Old Harry Rocks with something in hand.

Ran poorly next time at Doncaster, finishing a 23-lengths fourth of 13 to Black Op in a Class 6 bumper.

Fifth foal and a full brother to bumper/hurdle/chase winner Montys Meadow and Minella Awards, a winner up to three miles. Dam is an unraced half-sister to 2m 2f hurdle winner Supreme Ruler from the family of Grand National winner Monty's Pass.

Described by his trainer as being a 'bit buzzy' and affected by 'growing pains' last season, but is well regarded and looks just the sort his handler does well with. Likely to prove most effective in novice hurdles over two and a half miles or more.

OUTOFTHISWORLD (4YR BAY FILLY)

TRAINER:	**Harry Fry**
PEDIGREE:	**Shantou – Mystic Masie (Turgeon)**
FORM:	**1 -**
OPTIMUM TRIP:	**2m 4f**

Showed a bright turn of foot and a good attitude when winning a bumper at Market Rasen on her sole start last season.

Settled in just behind the leaders, came through smoothly two furlongs from home before quickening clear to beat Jane Lamb by a long-looking 11 lengths.

Second foal of an unraced half-sister to the useful Toubab from the family of a 1m 2f Listed-placed winner Majorica Queen.

Looks an ideal type for the mares' hurdle programme.

QUICK PICK (6YR BAY GELDING)

TRAINER:	Jennie Candlish
PEDIGREE:	Vinnie Roe – Oscars Arrow (Oscar)
FORM:	0212 -
OPTIMUM TRIP:	2m 4f

Shaped well in Irish point-to-points, runner-up on his second start and beating Doc Carver, a winner next time, by five lengths at Ballyragget in March.

Was a little fractious at the gate before his UK debut but ran well, staying on in the straight to finish second to the highly impressive Not That Fuisse, with subsequent dual-bumper winner Equus Amadeus half-a-length behind in third.

Dam comes from the family of Gold Cup winner Captain Christy.

Looks well bought for £12,000 by these connections four days after winning his point-to-point. Likely to benefit from a distance of ground in time.

RIO QUINTO (4YR BAY GELDING)

TRAINER:	Olly Murphy
PEDIGREE:	Loup Breton – Seal Of Cause (Royal Academy)
FORM:	3 - 2
OPTIMUM TRIP:	2m 4f

Acquired for £130,000 at Cheltenham's Tattersalls Sale in June having shaped with promise in point-to-points at Broughshane and Dromahane.

Made his debut at Broughshane in April, starting favourite and running on into third beaten one and three-quarter lengths by The Holy One. Ran a similar sort of race at Dromahane a month later, finishing a one-length second to Reasonable Doubt, again keeping on well to the line.

Seventh foal and a half-brother to Seldom Found, successful up to a mile and a half in France, out of an unraced half-sister to French Listed hurdle winner Some One.

Did not look a natural over fences but has been singled out for special mention by the trainer.

RUN TO MILAN (5YR BAY GELDING)

TRAINER:	**Victor Dartnall**
PEDIGREE:	**Milan – Run Supreme (Supreme Leader)**
FORM:	**1(disq)0 -**
OPTIMUM TRIP:	**2m +**

Showed plenty of ability when beating subsequent Grade 2 Aintree bumper winner Lalor at Wincanton on Boxing Day. Subsequently disqualified on a technicality.

Reappeared in April at Aintree but found the occasion too much to cope with, racing keenly and dropping away to finish 15 lengths behind the winner.

Eighth foal and a full brother to 3m hurdle winner City Supreme out of an unraced half-sister to the useful Old Flame and No Discount, a winner up to three miles.

Rider not hard on him once he was beaten at Aintree. Had schooled well at home last spring and expected to make a decent novice hurdler.

SALSARETTA (4YR BAY FILLY)

TRAINER:	Willie Mullins
PEDIGREE:	Kingsalsa – Kendoretta (Kendor)
FORM:	302 –
OPTIMUM TRIP:	2m +

Formerly trained in France by Francois Nicolle, ran three times over hurdles in 2016 at Auteuil.

Shaped well on her debut in May, 2016, finishing third in a Listed race to Dans La Foulee – subsequent dual-winner Tavera in second – before finishing down the field later that month over an extended 2m 1f. Showed much improved form on her return in September, finishing a short-neck second to D'Vina, later second in two Grade 3 races, over 2m 2f.

Missed the remainder of the season through sickness but form entitles her to respect as a seriously promising novice hurdler for the new season.

SAO (3YR BAY GELDING)

TRAINER:	Paul Nicholls
PEDIGREE:	Great Pretender – Miss Country (Country Reel)
FORM:	F - 1
OPTIMUM TRIP:	2m

Atoned for a fall on his hurdling debut at Auteuil in April when beating Hell Boy by a length and a quarter at Compiegne in May.

Third foal and a half-brother to this stable's talented Frodon and hurdle winner Tidjy. Dam French 2m 2f hurdle winner

Frodon – the half brother of Sao

and a half-sister to the very useful Medermit and 2m 5f chase winner Rangi.

Will be useful if he jumps as well as his half-brother Frodon.

SENATUS (5YR BAY GELDING)

TRAINER:	**Karen McLintock**
PEDIGREE:	**Early March – Winter Brook (Al Nasr)**
FORM:	**2100 -**
OPTIMUM TRIP:	**2m +**

Shaped with great promise in bumpers in 2016, second of 13 on his debut at Uttoxeter in May and a winner by five lengths at Musselburgh in November, challenging on the bridle and then responding well to driving.

Outclassed when sent south the following month for a Listed bumper at Ascot, finishing last but one after a brief flurry two furlongs from home. Started slowly and again pulled hard in a Class 2 bumper at Newbury in March (hooded for the first time).

Has subsequently shaped in encouraging fashion on the Flat, being campaigned as if middle-distance handicaps are the plan.

Has not been seen on the track since June but assuming all is well looks sure to win a novice event or two before continuing his career in handicaps. One of the more interesting horses in this section.

SHARJAH (4YR BAY GELDING)

TRAINER:	Willie Mullins
PEDIGREE:	Doctor Dino – Saaryeh (Royal Academy)
FORM:	02/442123 -
OPTIMUM TRIP:	2m

Has run eight times on the Flat in France, runner-up over 1m 2f on his second start at two and then a winner of an extended 1m 4f conditions race on the Polytrack at Deauville in July, 2016.

Second next time over the same course and distance and then third to subsequent Group 2 placed Travelling Man at Saint-Cloud in September, 2016.

Showed perfectly respectable form in France and has the profile to become a useful novice hurdler.

SNEAKY FEELING (5YR BAY GELDING)

TRAINER:	Philip Hobbs
PEDIGREE:	Oscar – Shuil Aris (Anshan)
FORM:	43101 –
HURDLE RATING:	135
OPTIMUM TRIP:	2m 4f +

Showed a modicum of ability when fourth of 11 in a point-to-point at Athlacca in May, 2016. Made his debut for this yard in a bumper at Market Rasen in November and then surprised connections when beating Bags Groove at 25/1 in a novices' hurdle at Newbury in December.

Could not cope with the step up to Grade 2 company next time at Cheltenham in January before returning to winning ways at Sandown in March, beating Mr Clarkson by 22 lengths.

First foal of bumper/hurdle/chase winning half-sister to 3m chase winner Hard To Get Ten and hurdle winner Larnalee from the family of Baronet and Liss A Paoraigh.

Expected to develop into a decent staying novice chaser.

STORM HOME (5YR BROWN GELDING)

TRAINER:	**Colin Tizzard**
PEDIGREE:	**King's Theatre – Miss Mayberry (Bob Back)**
FORM:	**F -**
OPTIMUM TRIP:	**2m 4f +**

Shaped very well before falling at the last with the race at his mercy in a point-to-point at Largy in April, 2016.

Race was won by Getabird, a subsequent dual-bumper winner for Willie Mullins and Rich Ricci, with a subsequent winner further behind.

Sold for £130,000 to this trainer in November, 2016, but didn't appear on the track.

Seventh foal and a three-parts brother to a point-to-point winner out of an unraced half-sister to chase winner Wests Awake from the family of The Romford Pele.

Evidently has plenty of ability and is more than interesting, whatever plans are in store for him this season.

STORMY MILAN (4YR BAY GELDING)

TRAINER:	Charlie Longsdon
PEDIGREE:	Milan – Socialite Girl (Glacial Storm)
FORM:	Unraced
OPTIMUM TRIP:	2m 4f +

Unraced for former trainer Colin Bowe, but showed him plenty of ability on the gallops and has pleased his new handler in early work.

Fourth foal and a full brother to point-to-point winner Llangwm Lad out of a half-sister to Wizard Bridge, a winner over hurdles and chases up to three miles, from the family of 3m chase winner Shining Willow.

Has been given some early schooling but expected to be confined to bumpers this season. Will stay a distance of ground in time.

STRONG PURSUIT (7YR CHESTNUT GELDING)

TRAINER:	Philip Hobbs
PEDIGREE:	Flemensfirth – Loughaderra (Strong Gale)
HURDLE RATING:	139
FORM:	F31/011P2 –
OPTIMUM TRIP:	2m 4f +

Bought by Aiden Murphy for £90,000 at Cheltenham's April Sale in 2015 having won the third of his three point-to-points by 15 lengths from The Tailor Quigley, who won next time out.

Made his stable debut for this yard in an extended 2m 5f Class 2 contest at Ascot last November, leading for a long way until blundering at the last. Made all to beat Chocola a month later

Flemensfirth – after one of his victories on the Flat

at Wincanton and repeated the tactics to win over an extended 2m 3f at Hereford in January. Was pulled up after taking a keen hold next time at Doncaster before running second to Reigning Supreme over an extended 2m 4f at Newbury in March.

Needs to relax more, but reported to have done well through the summer and expected to make his mark as a novice chaser.

SYMPA DES FLOS (5YR CHESTNUT GELDING)

TRAINER:	**Willie Mullins**
PEDIGREE:	**Tiger Groom – Je Te Donne (Mansonnien)**
FORM:	**2/**
OPTIMUM TRIP:	**2m +**

Comes with risks attached, having not seen the track for two years, but shaped very well on his sole start when second of 11 to Favorito Buck's in a 2m 2f Listed hurdle race at Auteuil in September, 2015.

Held up but did good late work to finish never nearer beaten eight lengths. Form of the race only moderate, with the winner beaten in five starts for Paul Nicholls.

Rated a useful prospect if he can be kept sound.

TETRAITES STYLE (5YR BAY GELDING)

TRAINER:	Nicky Richards
PEDIGREE:	Court Cave – Kilmessan (Flemensfirth)
FORM:	4 -
OPTIMUM TRIP:	2m 4f

Caught the eye in a major way on his debut at Newcastle in March, travelling well for much of the trip and still on the bridle just three lengths off the leader turning for home.

Steadily lost his place thereafter under considerate handling, finishing a tired fourth 29 lengths behind stable companion Reivers Lad.

Third foal and a full brother to 2m 5f hurdle winner Courtinthemiddle out of an unraced sister to 3m hurdle/chase winner Cheat The Cheater and a half-sister to 3m 1f hurdle/chase winner Takagi and 3m hurdle/chase winner Victrix Gale.

Gave the flights plenty of air at Newcastle, jumping as if fences would be more his game. Travelled like a useful horse for a long way, showing more than enough ability to win a novice event at some point this season.

One to note for both this season and the longer term.

THE BIG BITE (4YR BAY GELDING)

TRAINER:	Tom Lacey
PEDIGREE:	Scorpion – Thanks Noel (Tel Quel)
FORM:	1 -
OPTIMUM TRIP:	2m 4f +

A gawky but very promising type, who did well to win a bumper around Lingfield in view of his stout pedigree and inexperience.

Very green in the early stages but despite coming wide round the home turn found a decent turn of foot to quicken through and beat previous winner and subsequent hurdle winner Polly's Pursuit by three and a half lengths going away.

Fourth foal of an unraced half-sister to high-class bumper/hurdle/chase winner Cooldine from the family of Brackenheath and Brackenfield.

Had shown something at home prior to his victory but still did very well to win around such a tight track.

Carried head a little high but nothing to fault with his attitude and could make up into a useful hurdler, especially when stepped up to two and a half miles or more.

UNCLE ALASTAIR (5YR BAY GELDING)

TRAINER:	Nicky Richards
PEDIGREE:	Midnight Legend – Cyd Charisse (Kayf Tara)
FORM:	11 -
OPTIMUM TRIP:	2m 4f +

Very tenacious winner of both his bumper races, the first at Wetherby in January and the second at Ayr in February.

Victory looked unlikely for a long way on both occasions, only getting up to win by a neck each time. Required firm driving before responding at Wetherby and looked held in fourth a furlong from home at Ayr before staying on dourly to get up within a few strides of the post.

Second foal of a mare that won up to 2m 6f over hurdles who is a sister to 2m 4f/2m 5f winner Kayf Commander from the family of top-class Flat mare Cormorant Wood.

Has a pedigree more predisposed to stamina than speed and that is, indeed, how he runs.

Has the ability to win at two miles but the sooner he is asked to tackle a longer trip the better. Just the type of horse suited to this most patient of handlers.

WAR SOUND (8YR BAY GELDING)

TRAINER:	**Philip Hobbs**
PEDIGREE:	**Kayf Tara – Come The Dawn (Gunner B)**
HURDLE RATING:	**148**
FORM:	**1510/10/**
OPTIMUM TRIP:	**2m 4f +**

Has always worked like a top-class horse at home – there was once mention of the Champion Hurdle as a possible target – but injuries have kept him off the track including last season, when he aggravated a joint problem.

Made an impressive debut at Exeter on New Year's Day in January, 2015, winning an extended 2m 2f novices' hurdle by 12 lengths from Southfield Royale. Returned there just over a month later and finished down the field behind Native River after pulling hard.

Returned to winning ways in March, beating Floresco by six lengths in a 2m novices' hurdle at Chepstow. Not disgraced next time at Aintree, finishing in mid-division from a mark of 143, before landing the valuable Swinton Hurdle at Haydock in May off 140.

Was then off the track until February, 2016, finishing down the field in the Betfair Hurdle. Not seen out since.

Has schooled well over fences and expected to make up for lost time in his new discipline. Travelled powerfully in his hurdle races and has the potential to take high rank as a novice chaser provided he remains sound. Bred to stay very well.

War Sound – will be trying to make up for lost time

WHO'S MY JOCKEY (4YR BAY GELDING)

TRAINER:	Philip Hobbs
PEDIGREE:	Yeats – Scandisk (Kenmare)
FORM:	1 -
OPTIMUM TRIP:	2m 4f +

Made hard work of winning a Class 6 Bumper at Market Rasen in April, idling once he struck the front. Third, beaten a neck, won a maiden hurdle at Worcester next time out.

Cost €120,000 as a foal and €60,000 as a three-year-old store. Full brother to Blixt, a winner up to three miles over hurdles, from the family of the top-class performer Hurricane Fly.

Form nothing to write home about but very well regarded and expected to do well in staying novice hurdles.

WINTER SOLDIER (4YR BAY GELDING)

TRAINER:	Willie Mullins
PEDIGREE:	Soldier Hollow – Wintersonne (Big Shuffle)
FORM:	2
OPTIMUM TRIP:	2m

Ran second in a 1m 3f Flat race at Nantes as a three-year-old in April, 2016.

By the same sire as Arctic Fire and has a similar profile to that horse, having been with the same trainer in France.

Has shaped well in preliminary work at home and rated one of owner Rich Ricci's better prospects.

THE DARK HANDICAPPERS

The following horses appear to have something in hand of their current marks in the handicap.

CHAPEL STILE (5YR BAY GELDING)

TRAINER:	Nicky Richards
PEDIGREE:	Scorpion – Peggy Cullen (Presenting)
HURDLE RATING:	96
FORM:	0000 –
OPTIMUM TRIP:	2m 4f +

Has a similar profile to other slow-maturing staying prospects from this yard, having been brought along steadily in his novice season with a view to starting from an attractive platform in handicaps.

Looked distinctly moderate in four appearances last season, behind from the outset and jumping hesitantly in heavy ground on his first three starts, beaten a total of 100 lengths, before attracting market support from a mark of 99 for his handicap debut at Ayr in March.

Ridden up with the pace on that occasion but started to struggle down the far side and steadily lost his place to finish a well-beaten fifth of eight, 46 lengths behind the winner.

Was dropped 3lb to 96 following that run, his fourth on heavy going.

Sixth foal and a half-brother to the useful Rathvinden, a winner over hurdles and fences at up to three miles, bumper/hurdle winner Savingforvegas and point-to-point winner Bobby

Cullen. Dam unraced and a daughter of 3m hurdle winner Maries Gale.

Has shown precious little on the track but warrants another chance on better ground, perhaps over a longer trip.

CONQUER GOLD (7YR BAY MARE)

TRAINER:	Nicky Richards
PEDIGREE:	Gold Well – Ballinamona Wish (Kotashaan)
CHASE RATING:	123
FORM:	221/221/002214 -
OPTIMUM TRIP:	3m

Lightly raced mare, with the potential to improve further over a distance of ground.

Won the third of her three starts in Irish point-to-points, winning by ten lengths at Tinahely in March, 2015. Second at Carlisle that December in her sole start in a bumper before running second in an extended 3m maiden hurdle in January, 2016. Won over an extended 2m 7f at Hexham three months later.

Tried in handicap hurdles last autumn, beaten twice off 120 at Ayr, before switching to fences at Kelso in January. Ran well over an extended 2m 7f on her chasing debut, battling on bravely in the closing stages but beaten by the in-form Two Smokin Barrels.

Ran a similar sort of race next time over 3m 1f at Catterick, keeping on well to finish second, before winning a 3m 0-130 mares' chase at Bangor, despite not finding the ground as soft as she would have liked.

Shaped far better than her finishing position suggests when fourth of 12 to Magic Money on her final start in a 2m 6f handicap chase at Haydock, up there for a long way and keeping on bravely in the straight despite looking beaten leaving the back straight. Would have preferred softer ground.

Favourably treated on 123 and could prove effective from that mark in a staying handicap chase this winter. Has a great attitude with the stamina to match.

ELLENS WAY (5YR BAY MARE)

TRAINER:	Jeremy Scott
PEDIGREE:	Black Sam Bellamy – Function Dreamer (Overbury)
HURDLE RATING:	120
FORM:	3/2001 -
OPTIMUM TRIP:	2m 4f +

Showed promise in two point-to-points in Ireland, third to Whatduhavtoget – now rated on 130 with Dan Skelton – and then runner-up to subsequent bumper winner Redhotfillypeppers, now with Willie Mullins, at Necarne in May, 2016.

Ran a fair first race over hurdles behind Colin's Sister over 2m 5f at Warwick in November, 2016, and then seventh of 18 over an extended 2m 2f at Exeter before beating Copper Kay, winner of two of her next three races and now rated on 135, by a head at Warwick last December.

Sixth foal out of an unraced half-sister to useful hurdler/ chaser Captain Chris.

Met with a minor setback after Warwick but all now said to be fine. Collateral lines of form suggest she is very favourably treated on a mark of 120 although there is the option of going chasing.

Whatever the plan those close to the mare believe she has more to offer. Enjoys soft ground and will stay three miles.

LORD BALLIM (7YR CHESTNUT GELDING)

TRAINER:	**Nigel Hawke**
PEDIGREE:	**Balko – Lady Pauline (Hamas)**
CHASE RATING:	**127**
FORM:	**4P3F/0F0F33/300P2111U1 - 0**
OPTIMUM TRIP:	**2m 4f +**

Showed only a modicum of ability as a young horse in France and took a while to find his way after joining this yard in the spring of 2015, running placed on occasions switching between hurdles and fences.

Caught the eye in a major way and looked by far the best horse in the race when second, beaten a head, by Present Times in a 2m 3f 0-100 handicap hurdle at Towcester in February, still six lengths behind jumping the last and staying on strongly all the way to the line.

Duly atoned for that next time at Carlisle, dropped back to 2m 1f and keeping on well close home to beat Hartside by a neck from a mark of 105. Won again back there in April over an extended 2m 3f from 111 and then again when switched to fences in a 2m 4f handicap chase, winning by five lengths from Baileys Concerto.

Unseated rider when travelling well next time at Perth but won a 2m 4f 0-140 novices' handicap chase back there two days later (120). Down the field on his final start at Perth in June.

A strong-travelling sort who generally jumps well. Chase mark rose from 101 in March, 2016, to 127 by the end of last season but may still be at the right end of the handicap.

MIDNIGHT MAESTRO (5YR BAY GELDING)

TRAINER:	Alan King
PEDIGREE:	Midnight Legend – Calamintha (Mtoto)
HURDLE RATING:	126
FORM:	1/1021P –
OPTIMUM TRIP:	2m +

Lightly raced sort, who won a bumper at Doncaster in March, 2016, on his racecourse debut.

Made a successful hurdling debut at Warwick the following November, but down the field the following month in a Class 3 novices' event a Cheltenham won by the useful Pingshou. Shaped better at Wincanton in February when a three-quarters of a length second to Sir Antony Browne before keeping on well to beat Brotherly Company by four lengths at Stratford in March. Was pulled up on his final start of the season at Haydock in April.

Alan King – set for another good season

Sixth foal and a full brother to useful 2m hurdler William H Bonney and a handful of other fair performers including winners at up to three miles.

Regular work partner to Yanworth at home and probably capable of winning from his current mark, perhaps over further than two miles.

Worth noting in handicap hurdles before he is switched to fences.

NIETZSCHE (4YR CHESTNUT GELDING)

TRAINER:	**Brian Ellison**
PEDIGREE:	**Poet's Voice – Ganga (Generous)**
HURDLE RATING:	**136**
FORM:	**2213113 –**
OPTIMUM TRIP:	**2m 2f +**

Has run 16 times on the Flat, now rated on a mark of 84, but still relatively unexposed over hurdles with just seven runs to his name.

Plugged on at one pace to finish second on his first two starts over hurdles at Wetherby last October and Newcastle in November before making most, racing a little keenly, to beat the useful Project Bluebook by a length at Catterick in December.

Failed to replicate that form with the runner-up next time at Musselburgh, 5lb worse off at the weights but never jumping fluently and hampered by a faller at the last. Returned to winning form next time, stepped up to an extended 2m 2f and settling better, beating Norse Light by two and a half lengths off 122 relishing the testing ground.

Up in trip again a week later to an extended 2m 3f and beat Alzammaar by half a length off 123 despite again taking a keen hold.

Proved suited to the bigger field and stronger pace on his final start in the Fred Winter Juvenile Handicap Hurdle at Cheltenham, tracking leaders and ridden to lead approaching the last and keeping on well, despite a last flight blunder, to be beaten two necks by the useful Flying Tiger and Divin Bere.

Only once had the bottomless ground last season his trainer says he needs and can win a top handicap hurdle from this mark given his conditions. Had a quiet spin on the Flat in September to put an edge on him for the new season.

ON A PROMISE (5YR GREY GELDING)

TRAINER:	**Nicky Richards**
PEDIGREE:	**Definite Article – Silvers Promise (Presenting)**
HURDLE RATING:	**91**
FORM:	**0000 –**
OPTIMUM TRIP:	**2m 4f +**

Showed little to the eye on his four starts last season, beaten an aggregate of 178 lengths, but would not be in this yard if those performances were an accurate measure of his potential.

Looked very inexperienced on his hurdling debut over an extended 2m 4f at Ayr in November, held up and travelling reasonably well until tiring and dropping away in the last half mile. Shaped in a similar manner back at two miles the following month at Kelso and again at Doncaster in January.

Rated on 98 following those three races and ran from that mark in an extended 2m 0-100 in heavy ground at Newcastle in February, jumping ponderously in arrears until making a little headway three out before tiring and dropping back, beaten 50 lengths.

Third foal out of an unraced half-sister to Local Show, a winner at up to three miles over hurdles and fences, from the family of the very useful Strong Promise.

Trainer a dab hand at bringing horses of this type along. Respect market support, especially when he is stepped up again in trip. Pedigree predisposes him to favouring good ground.

POP ROCKSTAR (5YR BAY GELDING)

TRAINER:	**Jonjo O'Neill**
PEDIGREE:	**Flemensfirth – Special Ballot (Perugino)**
HURDLE RATING:	**110**
FORM:	**0P0442 – 0**
OPTIMUM TRIP:	**2m +**

Showed promise on his sole start in Ireland for Adrian Maguire, finishing sixth of 13 in a bumper.

Was pulled up after taking a keen hold on his hurdling debut for this trainer at Fontwell last November. Shaped better than finishing position suggests a month later at Plumpton before running fourth of 13 to Robinshill at Ffos Las nine days later.

Again ran well stepped up to an extended 2m 3f in a novices' hurdle at Chepstow before finishing a 26-lengths' second to Allee Bleue from a mark of 114 on his handicap debut at Leicester in February.

Held up and never near to challenge on his return to action at Bangor this October.

Fourth foal and a half-brother to 2m 7f chase winner Uncle Pettit from the family of 3m hurdle/chase and useful Flat performer First Ballot and the very useful Grey Shot.

May be able to win a staying handicap hurdle from his mark but has the scope to prove a capable novice chaser.

UN NOBLE (7YR GREY GELDING)

TRAINER:	Nicky Richards
PEDIGREE:	Near Honor – Noble Gary (Loup Solitaire)
CHASE RATING:	120
HURDLE RATING:	113
FORM:	0/04010/3411P1/UPP4 – 0
OPTIMUM TRIP:	2m 4f +

Formerly useful performer, winning three times over fences in 2015/16 from marks of 113, 116 and 123. Looked set for a good season last autumn, but was never right and was pulled up twice before finishing down the field in a 2m 4f handicap chase and then eighth of 11 in a 3m handicap hurdle at Perth in May.

Was found to have ulcers and a back problem which have hopefully now been rectified.

Trainer wants to alternate the horse's races between hurdles and fences this season in the hope that it will see a return to winning ways.

Comes with risks attached, but nicely treated over hurdles especially if he can recover his best form.

WHAT ABOUT CARLO (6YR BAY GELDING)

TRAINER:	Eve Johnson Houghton
PEDIGREE:	Creachadoir – Boccatenera (Artan)
FORM:	64 -
OPTIMUM TRIP:	2m

An accomplished performer on the level, rated on 108 at the time of writing, but expected to make an impression over hurdles following a couple of educational outings last season.

What About Carlo – has the class to win a top handicap hurdle

Highly tried on his hurdling debut when finishing last of six behind Moon Racer in the Grade 2 Supreme Trial Novices' Hurdle at Cheltenham in November, tracking leaders before weakening from the second last.

Reappeared just over a month later in a maiden hurdle at Newbury, again weakening in the closing stages to finish fourth of 17 to High Bridge.

Requires one more run for a handicap mark but probably heading for a rating in the low to high 120s based on his form to date.

Has proved a very consistent performer on the Flat, winning seven of his 35 starts including a 1m 2f Listed contest at Newbury in July.

Loves soft ground and is one to have at the top of your list for the Betfair Hurdle at Newbury in February.

THE POINT-TO-POINT RECRUITS

JODIE STANDING

The 2016/17 Irish point-to-point season has been one of the strongest for some time, which has been reflected by record-breaking prices being made at the sales. There has also been evident a high level of ability in the English points. With so much talent to call upon it has been difficult to whittle down the numbers for this feature but I felt the following 40 graduates all warranted their place. Although they are all lightly raced, there has been sufficient promise in their performances to suggest they will prove effective once racing under Rules. They may, though, require time to reach their full potential.

ATAGUISEAMIX (4YR BAY GELDING)

TRAINER:	Paul Nicholls
PEDIGREE:	Al Namix – Olafane (Le Balafre)
FORM (P2P):	2 -
OPTIMUM TRIP:	2m +
GOING:	Soft

This sizeable son of Al Namix showed sufficient promise on his debut to suggest he will develop into a useful novice hurdler.

Ataguiseamix made his debut at The Pigeons in March, where he was sent off a shade of odds-on to beat a competitive five-runner field. The four-year-old was prominent throughout and jumped well on the soft ground, but found himself a little outpaced between the fences. He finished second, beaten two lengths by the Gigginstown-owned Valdieu who had the benefit of experience and has since run creditably in the valuable Goffs Land Rover Bumper at Punchestown behind the well-regarded Vision Des Flos.

This four-year-old is a big, rangy, chasing type and left the impression he would come on for his run and be seen to greater effect once he's had time to fully mature.

BALLYMOY (4YR BAY GELDING)

TRAINER:	**Nigel Twiston-Davies**
PEDIGREE:	**Flemensfirth – John's Eliza (Dr Massini)**
FORM (P2P):	**4 - 33**
OPTIMUM TRIP:	**2m 4f +**
GOING:	**Good to Soft**

Ballymoy may not have the most appealing form figures, but he has gone to good connections and can pay his way this season.

The Flemensfirth gelding made his debut at Largy in April and didn't disgrace himself to finish fourth. Given a quiet ride towards the rear of the field, he made steady progress throughout and was only beaten 12 lengths having at no stage been asked for maximum effort. Next time at Necarne he again ran with promise in what was a strong maiden, won by a very progressive type in Good Man Pat.

Ballymoy left the impression that there was plenty left to work on in both his point-to-points. A half-brother to a 2m 4f winner, his dam was a bumper and hurdle winner up to 2m 4f and is a half-sister to the smart chaser Invictus.

The gelding made his Rules debut in a competitive bumper at Market Rasen at the beginning of October and acquitted himself well. Keen in the early stages, he was beaten by a well-backed individual, but he finished his race off nicely leaving the impression there is plenty more to come.

There is an ideal blend of speed and stamina in his pedigree. I expect him to do well for his new handler.

BATTLEOVERDOYEN (4YR BAY GELDING)

TRAINER:	**Gordon Elliott**
PEDIGREE:	**Doyen – Battle Over (Sillery)**
FORM (P2P):	**1 -**
OPTIMUM TRIP:	**2m 4f +**
GOING:	**Good**

This four-year-old looks to have a very bright future based on his impressive debut victory at Loughanmore in April.

Well punted before his race, the son of Doyen went off the evens favourite and looked a classy individual as he travelled with ease in mid-division under Mark O'Hare behind the strong pace.

Asked to take closer order after the third from home, the gelding moved on to the heels of the leaders jumping the penultimate fence but was forced to take evasive action to avoid two fallers on the landing side, leaving him slightly flat-footed. Ridden to mount a challenge rounding the turn for home he quickened up smartly and jumped the last alongside Court Liability and pulled out all that was necessary to finish well on top at the line.

Purchased for £235,000 by Gordon Elliott in April, this is a big, strong imposing gelding with great scope. He may, though, take time to fully mature.

BLACKBOW (4YR BAY GELDING)

TRAINER:	Willie Mullins
PEDIGREE:	Stowaway – Rinnce Moll (Accordion)
FORM (P2P):	1 -
OPTIMUM TRIP:	2m +
GOING:	Good to Soft

This big strong chasing type oozed class as he paraded around the ring before the sale at Aintree in April.

Blackbow went to the sales having scored decisively on his debut in an English point-to-point at Maisemore Park. Wearing

Willie Mullins – extraordinary strength in depth

a noseband, the gelding tracked the leaders travelling keenly before being produced to lead at the third from home. Still taking a strong grip approaching the penultimate fence, the four-year-old slightly fluffed his lines by blundering but it did little to stall his momentum and he went to the last with a two-length lead. Slightly overjumping the fence, he landed steeply which gave his rival a chance, but he regathered his stride and quickened up smartly to go away at the finish to win by two lengths from Canelo.

Given his imposing stature this son of Stowaway could take time to come to hand, but he is an exciting prospect and Willie Mullins obviously liked what he saw as he paid £150,000 to take the gelding home.

BREWIN'UPASTORM (4YR BAY GELDING)

TRAINER:	Dan Skelton
PEDIGREE:	Milan – Daraheen Diamond (Husyan)
FORM (P2P):	1 -
OPTIMUM TRIP:	2m +
GOING:	Good to Soft

Brewin'Upastorm was a very impressive eight lengths debutant winner in a point-to-point at Quakerstown in April.

The son of Milan travelled supremely well on the heels of the leaders, jumping efficiently before being asked to take closer order on the run down the hill towards the penultimate fence. Quickening smartly he met the fence on a good stride, touching down with a narrow advantage, before pouring on the pressure on the run to the last. Nothing could go with the four-year-old as he quickened away jumping the final fence with an eight-length lead which he easily maintained all the way to the line.

He will run in the colours carried by Robin Roe and Knockgraffon and will be trained by Dan Skelton having been purchased by Ryan Mahon for a hefty £250,000 in April.

A full brother to Get Back In Line, trained by Jonjo O'Neill to win a 2m3f hurdle race, he is closely related to 2m Flat winner and later 2m 4f chase winner Glam Gerry along with a couple of other winners.

This is a pedigree packed with winners and Brewin'Upastorm looks ready to carry on the good work.

CAREFULLY SELECTED (5YR BAY GELDING)

TRAINER:	**Willie Mullins**
PEDIGREE:	**Well Chosen – Knockamullen Girl**
	(Alderbrook)
FORM (P2P):	**21 -**
OPTIMUM TRIP:	**2m 4f +**
GOING:	**Good to Soft**

This is a talented but quirky individual with the potential to be very smart if his temperament can be satisfactorily addressed.

The son of Well Chosen made an eye-catching debut at Oldtown in February when finishing runner-up in a competitive five-year-old geldings' maiden. Once hitting the front after the penultimate fence, he ran very green and almost became unrideable jumping the last which probably ended up costing him the race.

Benefiting from that experience, he was seen next time out in a similar event at Monksgrange. Given a confident ride by Katie Walsh, who took the mount for her father, she held up the five-year-old at the rear of the field before making stealthy progress at the fifth from home, producing him to go in pursuit of the leader with a good jump three from the finish. Quickly eating into the advantage, the gelding was upsides jumping the penultimate fence and soon put daylight between himself and his rival. A slight jink on the approach to the last had favourite backers holding their breath for a moment, but a tidy leap secured the race.

Willie Mullins and Harold Kirk paid £100,000 for the gelding at the Cheltenham Sales in June. Providing he can iron out his quirks he could be a smart individual. Katie Walsh speaks highly of him.

CHOOSEYOURWEAPON (4YR BAY GELDING)

TRAINER:	Evan Williams
PEDIGREE:	Flemensfirth – Definite Love (Definite Article)
FORM (P2P):	1 -
OPTIMUM TRIP:	2m 4f +
GOING:	Good to Soft

Connections went to £210,000 for this good-looking son of Flemensfirth.

Chooseyourweapon was one of five newcomers when making his debut at Inch in April, but he clearly knew his job as he obliged with the minimum amount of fuss.

The gelding hit the front jumping the fourth from home and continued to dispute the lead with the Gigginstown-owned Desire De Joie on the run to the next. Responding well to a shake of the reins, the four-year-old pricked his ears taking the third from home and landed a length clear. Touching down with momentum, the gelding continued to run on strongly, repelling the challenge from the favourite Turtle Wars.

A slight blunder at the penultimate fence did little to stop him as he steadily increased his advantage, eventually going on to score by an easy six lengths.

The four-year-old looks a real staying sort, but he also possesses a turn of foot which will be seen to good effect if he runs in a bumper.

COOL GETAWAY (5YR BAY GELDING)

TRAINER:	Gordon Elliott
PEDIGREE:	Getaway – Coolnacarriga (Saddlers' Hall)
FORM (P2P):	1 -
OPTIMUM TRIP:	2m 4f +
GOING:	Soft

The sire Getaway has been all the rage at the sales and this one went the way of Margaret O'Toole for the sum of £305,000 following a gutsy and polished debut success at Tattersalls Farm last November.

Visibility was poor at the venue, but this was a strongly contested maiden with plenty of well-bred individuals making their debuts for top stables.

Cool Getaway was held up in the mid-division for much of the contest but took closer order at the third from home, almost touching down in front on the landing side. On the run to the penultimate fence the gelding produced a sharp turn of foot which quickly took a few lengths out of the field. He had to overcome a blunder at the last, which had his nose on the floor, but he regathered his stride and was well on top at the line, eventually winning by three lengths from King Of Kilmeague, who is now in training with Paul Nicholls.

The form of the point has been franked several times since, confirming that this was a strong contest.

Cool Getaway is a half-brother to bumper and hurdle winner Cloudy Rock and his dam, who won a bumper, is a half-sister to Jonjo O'Neill's classy Shutthefrontdoor.

COPPER GONE WEST (4YR BAY FILLY)

TRAINER:	Tim Vaughan
PEDIGREE:	Westerner – Copper Dusht (Dushyantor)
FORM (P2P):	1 -
OPTIMUM TRIP:	2m +
GOING:	Good to Soft

Tim Vaughan parted with £100,000 to bring this daughter of Westerner home from Cheltenham in April.

Copper Gone West caught the eye travelling smoothly off the pace on her debut at Inch before making noticeable headway to make ground on the leaders shortly after halfway. A slight mistake at the fourth from home did little to halt her momentum and she was vying for the lead when left in front by a faller at the third from home. Still not asked for maximum effort, the filly started to pull clear jumping the penultimate fence and, despite hanging marginally on the approach to the last, she popped over nicely to quicken away on the climb to the line.

The four-year-old has a lovely pedigree packed full of quality. Her dam is a half-sister to the useful Copper Bleu, Cloudy Copper, Give Me A Copper and Presenting Copper (dam of Copper Kay) who won this point-to-point 11 years ago.

The filly may not be the flashiest of horses but she has plenty of ability.

COURT LIABILITY (4YR BAY GELDING)

TRAINER:	**Harry Whittington**
PEDIGREE:	**Court Cave – Whataliability**
	(Leading Counsel)
FORM (P2P):	**2 -**
OPTIMUM TRIP:	**2m +**
GOING:	**Good**

Harry Whittington went through a quiet spell with his horses last season when they weren't quite right. He'll be hoping for better luck this time around and Court Liability could be a useful prospect for him.

The son of Court Cave lost nothing in defeat when finishing runner-up to the impressive winner Battleoverdoyen, who then went the way of Gordon Elliott for £235,000. This gelding, bought for £88,000, jumped supremely well throughout the 3m contest at Loughanmore and took up the running at the third from home. Still with a slight advantage jumping the last, he was unable to sustain his gallop but displayed great resolution and determination to battle with the three-length winner on the run-in.

The four-year-old's attitude will stand him in good stead once racing under Rules and I expect him to be competitive in novice hurdle events on good ground. His trainer says he is a big chasing type who jumps very well.

CRACKING DESTINY (4YR BAY GELDING)

TRAINER:	Nicky Henderson
PEDIGREE:	Dubai Destination – Cracking Gale (Alderbrook)
FORM (P2P):	1 -
OPTIMUM TRIP:	2m 4f +
GOING:	Soft

This four-year-old is from the family of First Lieutenant and appeared to love his racing when making a winning debut at Horse and Jockey in March.

Cracking Destiny went to the front from the drop of the flag and took the six-strong field along at a good pace. Always travelling well within himself, the son of Dubai Destination stretched to a two-length advantage jumping the penultimate fence which soon had his nearest pursuers all off the bridle.

Jumping the last he appeared to have the race in safekeeping when Daly Tiger, who was in the midst of throwing in a late bid, took a tumble and exited the race along with the horse back in third, which left the only other finisher trailing 30 lengths behind.

Cracking Destiny showed a willing attitude from the front which should stand him in good stead under Rules.

DORRELLS PIERJI (4YR BROWN GELDING)

TRAINER:	**Willie Mullins**
PEDIGREE:	**Coastal Path – Playa Pierji (Sleeping Car)**
FORM (P2P):	**1 -**
OPTIMUM TRIP:	**2m +**
GOING:	**Good to Soft**

The sky looks the limit for Dorrells Pierji judging by the runaway nature of his success at Belharbour in February.

It didn't take long before it became apparent that the son of Coastal Path was distinctly above average as he jumped with great athleticism and accuracy at the head of affairs. Displaying a high cruising speed, the four-year-old came to the fifth from home with a length advantage, which quickly became three on the run to the next.

Still hard on the bridle approaching three from home, his rivals were unable to get close enough to mount a challenge and Dorrells Pierji quickly went through the gears to pull away between the final two fences, opening up a 15-length lead jumping the last.

The gelding posted a quick time given that he sauntered home in nothing more than a canter.

This is a very exciting prospect to look forward to as he enters training with Willie Mullins for the same connections as Bacardys. He has the potential to take high rank.

FELIX DESJY (4YR CHESTNUT GELDING)

TRAINER:	Gordon Elliott
PEDIGREE:	Maresca Sorrento – Lamadoun (Smadoun)
FORM (P2P):	1 -
OPTIMUM TRIP:	2m +
GOING:	Soft

Felix Desjy announced himself on the pointing scene at Dromahane in March, coming home a very easy winner of an 11-runner maiden in the colours of Gigginstown.

Always prominent, the gelding took up the running at the fourth from home but was tracked by the fellow Gigginstown-owned Momus as the tempo began to lift. Galloping on relentlessly the pair soon opened up four lengths on the field and jumped the third last together.

On the approach to the penultimate fence the gelding displayed a devastating turn of foot which saw him go clear before flying over the last, propelling him up the run-in to win by a very impressive 15 lengths.

The turn of foot he showed was truly incredible and he looks a hugely exciting prospect for the new season.

He is surely one to note for bumpers given his change of gear.

GLENMONA (5YR BAY MARE)

TRAINER:	Harry Whittington
PEDIGREE:	Dubai Destination – Sabbiosa (Desert Prince)
FORM (P2P):	31 -
OPTIMUM TRIP:	2m
GOING:	Good to Soft

This speedy type has already shown promise on her first start for her new trainer.

The five-year-old made an eye-catching debut at Kirkistown in March where she was never a factor but hinted that she had ability by staying on well to take third towards the finish.

On her second outing two weeks later at Portrush, the daughter of Dubai Destination was ridden far more positively and was taken to the lead from the drop of the flag. She soon had an eight-length lead on the field and jumped well under Mark O'Hare until given a breather at the third from home, allowing the field to come back to her slightly. Still held by a tight rein, she began to come away from the field again on the approach to the penultimate fence and put the race into safekeeping with a brilliant leap at the last.

The five-year-old has a good ground action so may not have appreciated the soft underfoot conditions she experienced on her bumper debut at Stratford. However she showed great promise and stayed on well once headed up the home straight, suggesting a stiffer test once sent hurdling would suit.

GLOBAL CITIZEN (5YR BAY GELDING)

TRAINER:	Jonjo O'Neill
PEDIGREE:	Alkaadhem – Lady Willmurt (Mandalus)
FORM (P2P):	1 -
OPTIMUM TRIP:	2m +
GOING:	Good to Soft

This gelding looked well above average when scoring impressively at the first time of asking.

Global Citizen made his debut in what was an ordinary contest but he looked distinctly useful as he displayed a fine blend of speed and stamina on his way to victory. He was left in front at the ninth fence as he took the field along at a medium pace, jumping nicely before quickening readily on the approach to the penultimate fence. A spring-heeled leap there followed by a neat jump at the last allowed the gelding to come home at ease under Noel McParlan who never asked the son of Alkaadhem for maximum effort.

This full brother to A Hare Breath, who is highly regarded by Ben Pauling, is also a half-brother to the useful performer De Plotting Shed.

He appears to have plenty of pace and should make his presence felt in bumpers before being sent novice hurdling.

GOOD MAN PAT (4YR BAY GELDING)

TRAINER:	Alan King
PEDIGREE:	Gold Well – Basically Supreme (Supreme Leader)
FORM (P2P):	P - 1
OPTIMUM TRIP:	3m
GOING:	Soft

Good Man Pat was clearly well thought of on his debut to be sent off the evens favourite, but the four-year-old didn't do himself justice and pulled up before the penultimate fence.

He evidently benefited from the outing and put the experience to good use just two weeks later at Necarne when winning a 16-runner event. The son of Gold Well travelled comfortably throughout and displayed a devastating turn of foot to surge to the lead jumping the penultimate fence before staying on strongly down to the last. Popping over it he passed the line with plenty in hand to win by an easy 12 lengths from the 3/1 joint-favourite Present From Dubai.

Good Man Pat is an athletic and rangy gelding and will race in the yellow and red colours of David Sewell.

HEROESANDVILLAINS (4YR BAY GELDING)

TRAINER:	Noel Meade
PEDIGREE:	Beneficial – Keys Pride (Bob Back)
FORM (P2P):	3U1 -
OPTIMUM TRIP:	2m 4f +
GOING:	Soft/Heavy

This scopey gelding looks like he'll need plenty of time to reach his full potential.

The son of Beneficial gained a well-deserved success at the third time of asking when making all at Courtown in April, having not got further than the second fence at Loughbrickland the time before. He had displayed plenty of promise on his debut in March when finishing third behind two well-regarded types so it was only a matter of time before he got his head in front.

Sent to the lead from the drop of the flag the gelding set a steady tempo but always looked in control of a tightly bunched field in behind. Rounding the final turn he quickened up smartly, stretching his advantage to four lengths jumping the third from home. Still with plenty left in the tank the four-year-old was able to repel all challengers to win by two and a half lengths.

This looks decent form as the second-placed horse Clash Of D Titans now enters training with Warren Greatrex, fourth home Moonshine Bay subsequently went on to win by eight lengths on his next start and the sixth home, who was beaten by over 13 lengths, won cosily next time.

Heroesandvillains is a big stamp of a horse who looks as if he will need time to reach his peak.

HITMAN FRED (4YR BAY GELDING)

TRAINER:	Rose Dobbin
PEDIGREE:	Getaway – Garravagh Lass (Oscar)
FORM (P2P):	1
OPTIMUM TRIP:	2m 4f +
GOING:	Good to Soft

This gelding by the popular sire Getaway should be able to take advantage of novice hurdle events in the north when the emphasis is on stamina.

Rose Dobbin – getting a good string together

Hitman Fred made his debut at Bartlemy in May and looked a dour stayer as he came home powerfully to win by four lengths.

Jamie Codd clearly felt he had plenty of horse underneath him as he sat quietly on the gelding five lengths behind the leaders jumping the third from home. Once he had taken the fence, the four-year-old quickly changed gear and found himself in a threatening position on the turn for home. Still a couple of lengths down on the leaders jumping the penultimate fence, the gelding surged to the lead and battled on gallantly, never stronger than at the line.

This was a taking performance and Hitman Fred clearly possesses plenty of stamina. He looks a decent prospect for Rose Dobbin.

INDIAN HAWK (5YR BAY GELDING)

TRAINER:	Nicky Henderson
PEDIGREE:	Westerner – Yorkshire Girl (Anshan)
FORM (P2P):	2 - 1
OPTIMUM TRIP:	2m +
GOING:	Good to Soft

This classy gelding overcame a first fence scare when coasting to a 40-length success on his second start.

Indian Hawk was novicey on his debut at Charm Park in April when finishing second behind the more experienced Cheat Fairly, but he quickly overcame that inexperience on his next start when winning as he liked under Sam Burton at Tabley.

A first fence faller badly hampered the gelding and could easily have had his jockey on the floor, but defying gravity he managed to keep the partnership intact despite jumping the next fence without his irons. Once equilibrium was restored, Indian Hawk was able to travel round in nothing more than a canter, jumping well to stretch clear from the field on the final circuit.

The winning distance was officially 40 lengths and although he may not have beaten much, he could not have been much more impressive.

He now enters training with Nicky Henderson for owners Simon Munir and Isaac Souede.

KINGS MONARCH (4YR BAY GELDING)

TRAINER:	Kerry Lee
PEDIGREE:	Schiaparelli – Monarch's View (King's Ride)
FORM (P2P):	1
OPTIMUM TRIP:	2m 4f +
GOING:	Good

Kerry Lee has a nice bunch of youngsters this season and this four-year-old by up-and-coming sire Schiaparelli looks a decent acquisition having been bought for £60,000 from the Donnchadh Doyle stable.

The gelding, who was apparently the standout individual based on looks in the paddock, made his debut in what seemed to be an ultra-competitive maiden.

Always up with the pace from the drop of the flag, the four-year-old jumped into the lead at the fourth from home. Still travelling well within himself approaching three out he was

Kerry Lee – a fine record with mud-loving stayers

again spring-heeled, extending his advantage over his nearest pursuer.

Jumping the penultimate fence with ease the gelding had to be ridden away, but responded well for pressure and came to the last with ears pricked. A slight mistake there did not halt his momentum and he went on to score by three lengths from Some Ambition who had the benefit of two previous runs, winning in a time three seconds below the average for the day.

Kings Monarch hails from the family of high-class Graded performer Our Vic whose victories included the Grade 1 Ascot Chase and Grade 1 Ryanair Chase.

Having displayed plenty of speed on good ground I expect him to prove effective in bumpers before switching to hurdling.

KUPATANA (4YR BAY FILLY)

TRAINER:	Nicky Henderson
PEDIGREE:	Westerner – Kildea Cailin (Anshan)
FORM (P2P):	1 -
OPTIMUM TRIP:	2m +
GOING:	Good to Soft

This smart filly should have the pace to be competitive in bumpers.

Kupatana clearly knew her job when making her debut at Monksgrange in March. Sent off at odds of 4/1 she went to the front from flagfall and jumped incredibly well to quickly put daylight between herself and the field. Six lengths clear on the approach to the penultimate fence she jumped it well before quickening away in good style down to the last. Steadied into the fence she popped over and careered away to win by a very easy eight lengths.

Westerner – in his racing days

Purchased by Highflyer for the owners of River Wylde and Lough Derg Spirit, she will now go into training with Nicky Henderson.

This is a really likeable filly with plenty of size and scope.

MADISON TO MONROE (4YR ROAN GELDING)

TRAINER:	Jessica Harrington
PEDIGREE:	Presenting – Caltra Princess (Traditionally)
FORM (P2P):	1 -
OPTIMUM TRIP:	2m +
GOING:	Soft

Ann and Alan Potts have been splashing the cash this year and they dug deep to purchase this striking-looking gelding for £300,000.

The Aintree Sales topper went through the ring with a tall reputation having graduated from the same Monksgrange point-to-point that Samcro won prior to him being the sales topper 12 months earlier.

Madison To Monroe is a very unusually coloured roan – almost dappled grey – and he won his debut point-to-point in very easy fashion, recording the fastest time of the day. Always prominent under Barry O'Neill, the four-year-old went to the front from the halfway point and jumped very professionally bar one mistake at the fourth last where he got in tight.

To the eye he looks a real galloping sort, but his pedigree would suggest he has the speed to be competitive in bumpers before being sent over hurdles.

A half-brother to Westend Prince, who won over 2m 4f, his dam was a dual-purpose mare and is a half-sister to a seven-furlong performer.

The gelding's round action suggests that he will be more suited to soft conditions.

MAIRE BANRIGH (5YR BAY MARE)

TRAINER:	Dan Skelton
PEDIGREE:	King's Theatre – La Marianne (Supreme Leader)
FORM (P2P):	1 -
OPTIMUM TRIP:	2m +
GOING:	Good

This five-year-old broke the record for the most expensive point-to-point mare sold at public auction when John Hales and Ryan Mahon signed the docket for £320,000 at the Cheltenham Festival Sale in March.

The daughter of the late King's Theatre burst onto the scene with a very impressive victory in a mares' maiden event at Lingstown in March. Given a positive ride by Barry O'Neill, the five-year-old made every yard of the running and jumped impeccably to win on the bridle by five lengths. The form of the race looks strong, with three of the finishers in behind going on to win their maidens.

A half-sister to the useful hurdle and chase winner Ballykan, trained by Nigel Twiston-Davies, her dam was a bumper/hurdle winner and is a half-sister to that tough race mare Banjaxed Girl and also the useful Mountain King.

Maire Banrigh looks a quality mare and she covers the ground effortlessly. She is an exciting prospect for the months ahead.

MONBEG ZENA (5YR CHESTNUT MARE)

TRAINER:	Nicky Henderson
PEDIGREE:	Flemensfirth – Mandys Gold (Mandalus)
FORM (P2P):	1 -
OPTIMUM TRIP:	2m +
GOING:	Good/Soft

Another Nicky Henderson recruit, this mare won well on her debut point-to-point and could be one for novice hurdle events against her own sex, especially when the emphasis is on stamina.

Monbeg Zena was well supported in the market when making her debut in an above average mares' maiden at Ballinaboola. There was a searching gallop from the off which had several horses in trouble at an early stage, but the mare travelled supremely well and jumped accurately before making her move after the fourth from home.

Upsides and challenging for the lead at the next she touched down in front and steadily began to pull away from her rivals and jumped the penultimate fence with a length advantage. A slow jump at the last opened the door for her nearest pursuer, but she quickly regathered her stride and was well on top at the line.

The form of the race looks strong, with the runner-up having the race at his mercy next time when falling at the penultimate fence. Uisce Ur, who was 18 lengths behind Monbeg Zena, went on to win next time and Delgany Lass, back in sixth, won next time by five lengths.

This mare's previous handler Sean Doyle said after her victory that he thought the world of her but that they gave the daughter of Flemensfirth plenty of time as she was a big baby and didn't show much at home.

The five-year-old is a full-sister to Sizing Gold and a half-sister to hurdle winner Exxaro. She looks to have plenty of size and scope and should improve as she matures.

MOONSHINE BAY (4YR BAY GELDING)

TRAINER:	Colin Tizzard
PEDIGREE:	Milan – Chantoue Royale (Cadoudal)
FORM (P2P):	4 - 1
OPTIMUM TRIP:	2m 4f +
GOING:	Good to Soft

There looks to be plenty more to come from this imposing son of Milan who improved markedly from his debut to win easily on his second start.

Moonshine Bay made his debut at Courtown in early April, finishing fourth having not been able to go with the leaders when the pace began to quicken. That was on yielding to soft ground which may not have suited him.

Reappearing three weeks later on good ground at Loughrea, the gelding took up the running with a quick jump at the penultimate fence. From there on the race was in no doubt as he quickened up smartly, distancing himself from his rivals in a matter of strides. Ears pricked jumping the last, Jamie Codd kept the four-year-old up to his work to ensure an easy eight-length success.

This may not have been the strongest form in the book, but he looked a professional individual and has a pedigree packed with both speed and stamina.

A half-brother to 2m 7f winner Preseli Rock, 2m 4f hurdle winner Cinematique and bumper winner Westhorpe, his dam was a 1m 7f hurdle winner in France and was a sister to French 10f Group 3 winner Royale Chantou.

This well-bred individual can make his presence felt in bumpers on good ground.

MR LINGO (4YR BAY GELDING)

TRAINER:	Gordon Elliott
PEDIGREE:	Curtain Time – Pharlingo (Phardante)
FORM (P2P):	1 -
OPTIMUM TRIP:	2m 4f +
GOING:	Good

Now owned by Gigginstown, expectations will be high when this impressive debutant winner takes to the track.

Mr Lingo made his debut at Dromahane in April and quickly made a very good impression. The well-bred son of Curtain

Time travelled with ease on the heels of the leaders until taking up the running at the sixth from home.

Clearly enjoying the good ground conditions, the gelding bounded into a two-length lead jumping the penultimate fence and continued to stretch further clear on the run to the last. A flying leap there sent him scooting up the run-in to win by a very easy eight lengths from the 3/1 joint-favourite Impatient Partner who stayed on well to snatch second close home.

The form of the race looks strong, with several horses that finished behind going on to run creditably next time.

Mr Lingo hails from a family full of winners. A half-brother to Galway Plate winner Bob Lingo and jumps winner Talk The Lingo, his dam is a half-sister to the useful chase winner Dev.

This gelding is a very likeable type with plenty of size and scope, but he won't be seen at his best until tackling obstacles over trips in advance of 2m 4f.

NET DE TREVE (4YR BAY GELDING)

TRAINER:	Tom George
PEDIGREE:	Network – Dame De Treve (Cadoudal)
FORM (P2P):	2 -
OPTIMUM TRIP:	2m 4f +
GOING:	Soft

Net De Treve looked a work-in-progress on his debut at Inch and is now with Tom George having been acquired for €100,000.

The four-year-old was waited with in the rear under Derek O'Connor before making steady progress before halfway. Nudged along after the fourth from home, he was still being tenderly handled behind the main group of horses until urged to take closer order on the approach to the third last where he was untidy.

Allowed time to regather his stride, he jumped the next in fourth before surging down to the last, jumping it well and landing in second place. He continued to stay on strongly in the manner of a horse who would benefit greatly for the experience.

To the eye he looks an imposing sort with plenty of quality about him. He could turn out to be quite nice in time.

ON THE BLIND SIDE (5YR BAY GELDING)

TRAINER:	Nicky Henderson
PEDIGREE:	Stowaway – Such A Set Up (Supreme Leader)
FORM (P2P):	1 -
OPTIMUM TRIP:	2m +
GOING:	Soft

This debutant winner hails from the family of Knockara Beau, for so many years a stalwart of the northern jumping scene.

On The Blind Side posted a time on his debut at Kilfeacle which could only be matched by the classy track recruit Colour Squadron in the Open later in the afternoon. The race has subsequently produced a handful of winners and several creditable placed efforts, some from horses that are now racing under Rules.

The five-year-old caught the eye as he travelled with ease through the race and was soon on the heels of the leaders with a good jump at the third from home. Closely grouped jumping the penultimate fence, he readily went a couple of lengths clear on the landing side in response to a shake of the reins. Steadied into the final fence, his rivals came back at him but the son of Stowaway showed real grit and determination to rally once eyeballed up the run-in to win a shade cosily at the line.

Purchased for £205,000 in February by Highflyer for owner Alan Spence, reports of his work at home have been nothing but encouraging, and he should have enough pace to be competitive in a bumper.

PALMERS HILL (4YR BAY GELDING)

TRAINER:	Jonjo O'Neill
PEDIGREE:	Gold Well – Tosca Shine (Topanoora)
FORM (P2P):	31 -
OPTIMUM TRIP:	3m
GOING:	Good to Soft

This son of Gold Well has a huge amount of potential but may be kept for the latter half of the season when the ground is a little livelier.

Palmers Hill made his debut at Oldtown in arguably the most competitive maiden of the season where he bumped into the highly regarded but ill-fated Flemenshill and the 2016 Derby Sales topper Defi Bleu. There was plenty to like about this first outing, staying on well behind the winner, but he showed his true ability next time at Tyrella when scorching clear to win by 20 lengths under Jamie Codd.

The gelding was always travelling supremely well and took himself to the front with a bold leap at the second from home. Soon extending his advantage with an injection of pace, he came to the last in splendid isolation and jumped it well to come home with any amount in hand.

He was clearly in a different parish in terms of class to his rivals, displaying a fine attitude and a good turn of foot on ground conditions that were thought to be far from ideal. Now with Jonjo O'Neill, having been purchased by Kieran McManus for an eye-watering £310,000, the four-year-old is likely to be nurtured along with a spring campaign in mind.

PONTRESINA (4YR BAY GELDING)

TRAINER:	Oliver Sherwood
PEDIGREE:	Milan – Gilt Benefit (Beneficial)
FORM (P2P):	1 -
OPTIMUM TRIP:	2m +
GOING:	Soft

This interesting recruit looked above average on his debut in an English point-to-point at Eyton-On-Severn.

The four-year-old made virtually all of the running in the 2m 4f contest on ground described as good to soft, and displayed a fine attitude when challenged at the second from home. The son of Milan, whose jumping was a little sticky at times, came to the penultimate fence with very little in hand and looked likely to lose his lead jumping the fence. Head-to-head on the run to the last, he displayed the better turn of foot and pinged the fence to land with plenty of momentum, propelling him up the run-in to win by a cosy two lengths.

Serosevsky, who finished runner-up subsequently, went on to win his maiden in very easy fashion and now finds himself in the care of Harry Fry having been purchased for £60,000 at Goffs Horses In Training Sale in May. He too looks a decent prospect.

Oliver Sherwood purchased this gelding at the Tattersalls Cheltenham Sale in May for what could look a reasonable £40,000. He is from the family of Wrath Of Titans and Stopped, whom Sherwood will have known from his days as assistant trainer to Fred Winter.

POSH TRISH (4YR BAY FILLY)

TRAINER:	Paul Nicholls
PEDIGREE:	Stowaway – Moscow Demon
	(Moscow Society)
FORM (P2P):	1 -
OPTIMUM TRIP:	2m 4f +
GOING:	Good to Soft

This filly did well to win on her debut given that the conditions were incredibly testing.

Posh Trish was well supported in the market when making her debut at Lemonfield in a point-to-point which has produced a number of smart mares. She was always travelling powerfully through the race and, having taken up the running from an early stage, she had many of her rivals struggling thanks to some efficient jumping.

Two lengths clear jumping the penultimate fence, the daughter of Stowaway responded well to her jockey's urgings and quickened up smartly in the heavy conditions on the approach to the last. A slight blunder left the door open for the favourite Colreevy, who was coming out of the pack to challenge, but a mistake saw him exit the race and Posh Trish went on to win by 14 lengths.

The conditions of the race weren't ideal for the four-year-old who has a good ground action so it's testament to her ability that she was able to cope so well in the conditions.

Purchased for £135,000 she now enters training for Paul Nicholls to race in the colours of Highflyer.

SANTINI (5YR BAY GELDING)

TRAINER:	Dan Skelton
PEDIGREE:	Milan – Tinagoodnight (Sleeping Car)
FORM (P2P):	1 -
OPTIMUM TRIP:	2m +
GOING:	Good

This gelding displayed a scintillating round of jumping to come home unextended in his debut point-to-point.

The imposing son of Milan looked well above average as he dominated the eight-runner event at Didmarton. Jumping extremely well, the five-year-old took himself to the front at the fifth from home before edging clear along with one other rival on the run to the fourth last.

A flying leap saw him gain a length or two in the air and landing smartly he was soon five lengths clear and gone beyond recall. A blunder by his nearest pursuer at the third from home saw Santini well clear at the penultimate fence and he came away to jump the last with ears pricked, sauntering up the run-in to win by 15 lengths.

From a very smart family this five-year-old looks an exciting individual for Dan Skelton, who bought him for £150,000 at the Cheltenham Sale in March.

SENDING LOVE (4YR BAY GELDING)

TRAINER:	Willie Mullins
PEDIGREE:	Scorpion – Dato Vic (Old Vic)
FORM (P2P):	1 -
OPTIMUM TRIP:	2m +
GOING:	Good to Soft

This gelding looks as if he is blessed with a touch of class.

Sending Love made his debut at Kirkistown in February in a six-runner event, galloping to an easy five-length victory. The son of Scorpion sat towards the rear of the bunch for much of the contest before taking much closer order before the third from home.

Tanking up to the leader's quarters on the approach to the second last, the four-year-old was driven into the fence by Mark O'Hare and he responded generously to produce a mighty leap which took him to the front. From there on he stamped his authority to quickly scoot away to a five-length lead which he easily maintained once jumping the last.

This looks to be a gelding with plenty of substance and just the type his trainer excels in handling.

SLATE HOUSE (5YR BAY GELDING)

TRAINER:	Colin Tizzard
PEDIGREE:	Presenting – Bay Pearl (Broadway Flyer)
FORM (P2P):	5/1 -
OPTIMUM TRIP:	2m +
GOING:	Good to Soft

Slate House went into many people's tracker systems following Colin Tizzard's latest open day, when his son Joe gave this five-year-old as one of his horses to follow for the new season.

The son of Presenting did not show a great deal on his point-to-point debut in March 2016, but after being given plenty of time to strengthen by his former handler the gelding came back in November 2016 to score easily by ten lengths at Tattersalls Farm from Ring Moylan, who has since finished runner-up on both his starts for Jonjo O'Neill.

The form has also been franked by the third home, It's Your Move, now with Brian Ellison who has gone on to be placed on both his subsequent starts under Rules.

Slate House boasts a useful pedigree. He is a full brother to the Paul Nicholls-trained winner Touch Kick and a half-brother to hunter chase winner Repeat Business from the family of Big Buck's.

All the early portents and reports about this gelding have been very positive. He is one to keep a close eye on.

SOME MAN (4YR BAY FILLY)

TRAINER:	Paul Nicholls
PEDIGREE:	Beat Hollow – Miss Denman (Presenting)
FORM (P2P):	1 -
OPTIMUM TRIP:	2m 4f +
GOING:	Good to Soft

Some Man's reputation preceded him when he was sent off the evens favourite for his debut point-to-point at Portrush in March.

The son of Beat Hollow travelled with consummate ease through the race towards the rear of the field under a very confident Rob James. Asked to take closer order before the third from home, the response was immediate and he made rapid progress in a matter of strides, jumping the fence boldly and touching down in front. A quick squeeze from his jockey after the penultimate fence saw the four-year-old saunter away in effortless fashion under a motionless rider, jumping the last well to coast home by an unextended five lengths.

A half-brother to the very useful Polly Peachum, Le Dauphin and Polly's Pursuit out of a half-sister to Denman there is little wonder why everyone around the sales ring at Aintree wanted to sneak a peek at the four-year-old. The hammer was eventually knocked down to Highflyer for £165,000 acting on behalf of Paul Nicholls.

This is a racehorse with the world at his feet and he will be brought along quietly with a view to optimising his enormous potential.

STAY HUMBLE (4YR BAY GELDING)

TRAINER:	**Colin Tizzard**
PEDIGREE:	**Beat Hollow – Rosy De Cyborg (Cyborg)**
FORM (P2P):	**1 -**
OPTIMUM TRIP:	**2m +**
GOING:	**Good to Soft**

Here is another top prospect for the Colin Tizzard yard.

Stay Humble looked a class apart when he came home an easy winner on his debut at Ballynoe under Derek O'Connor.

Beat Hollow – an underrated sire

The Beat Hollow gelding sat just off the pace in the strongly run contest but made eye-catching progress as the race began to develop and he was quickly at the leader's quarters at the third from home. A good jump saw him land with forward momentum and he came to the penultimate fence with ears pricked and touched down in front.

A shake of the reins from his jockey saw him quicken up in the style of a good horse and he soon put daylight between himself and the rest. He popped the last and was allowed to gallop home in his own time to win by an eased down five lengths from Locker Room Talk, who has subsequently been purchased by Gearoid Costello for Rebecca Curtis for £135,000.

This half-brother to French hurdle and chase winner Une Lapin Rouge and point winner Smuggler's Blues is out of a mare who won over hurdles and is a full sister to the useful bumper and hurdle winner Rosy Cyborg.

It's early days, but Stay Humble looks to possess a touch of class and I expect him to prove more than useful, especially over a distance of ground.

STORM CONTROL (4YR BAY GELDING)

TRAINER:	Kerry Lee
PEDIGREE:	September Storm – Double Dream (Double Eclipse)
FORM (P2P):	1 -
OPTIMUM TRIP:	2m 4f +
GOING:	Soft/Heavy

This newcomer won a ten-runner event by an eased down 20 lengths at Lisronagh in April.

The son of September Storm travelled comfortably on the heels of the leaders before being produced to challenge at the fifth from home. A good jump three out saw the four-year-old start to pour on the pressure and extend his advantage before an excellent leap at the penultimate fence enabled him to go further clear. A slight mistake at the last did nothing to halt his momentum and he went on to win by a wide margin.

The form received a couple of notable boosts when Always Du Cerisier, who was beaten 22 lengths, went on to finish a good third next time while Good Man Pat, who was pulled up, went on to win a similar event next time by 12 lengths.

A full brother to the 2m hurdle winner Atlantic Storm, and half-brother to the smart hurdle and chase winner Tagrita, his dam is an unraced half-sister to the very gutsy Grey Abbey, who won two Grade 2 chases for Howard Johnson.

He looks a proper old-fashioned staying chaser in the making but it should be noted that he has a slight knee action so may be suited to softer conditions.

He is bred to stay very well on both sides of his pedigree. An exciting prospect.

STORM HOME (5YR BROWN GELDING)

TRAINER:	Colin Tizzard
PEDIGREE:	King's Theatre – Miss Mayberry (Bob Back)
FORM (P2P):	F/
OPTIMUM TRIP:	2m 4f +
GOING:	Good to Soft

Colin Tizzard has another potential star on his hands with this gelding.

Storm Home was in the midst of making a winning debut at Largy last April, but having slightly overjumped the last he crumpled on landing which gifted the race to the well-regarded Getabird, who has subsequently won three bumpers for Willie Mullins.

Up until his departure the King's Theatre gelding looked a classy individual, travelling with ease at the head of affairs and jumping with great accuracy and athleticism. Mark O'Hare was clearly feeling confident as he took a few leisurely looks over his shoulder after jumping the penultimate fence and he still had plenty of horse underneath him when taking the last.

Colin Tizzard has given the five-year-old plenty of time to mature and strengthen which should have done the horse the world of good. I expect him to develop into a smart type this season.

TEMPLEPARK (4YR BAY GELDING)

TRAINER:	Ben Case
PEDIGREE:	Phoenix Reach – Kenny's Dream (Karinga Bay)
FORM (P2P):	31 -
OPTIMUM TRIP:	3m
GOING:	Soft

Templepark, who was purchased for £75,000 by Kevin Ross Bloodstock, now finds himself in the care of Ben Case and is owned by Carolyn Kendrick whose amateur son Max is likely to ride him.

The gelding is an interesting performer and it's a surprise that he has not joined a higher-profile yard following a very professional and taking victory at Kirkistown in March. The gelding had made his debut at the same track in February to finish third after making late headway from the rear of the field.

Clearly benefiting from that run, the son of Phoenix Reach received a similar ride from Derek O'Connor who again anchored his mount out the back. Taking closer order coming to the third last, Templepark jumped out of his jockey's hands and touched down a couple of lengths clear of the field.

Once allowed a little rein, the gelding quickly opened up coming down the hill to string the field out on the approach to

Ben Case – does very well with the stock that comes his way

the penultimate fence where again he was bold. Appearing to be in third gear jumping the last, the four-year-old was allowed to come home in his own time to win by eight lengths from Spin The Coin in second place, with a further 10 lengths back to the third.

The strong pace of the race obviously suited Templepark as he was able to settle into a good rhythm before picking off his rivals as he liked.

This was a very taking performance and it will be interesting to see how he gets on for his new connections.

THE DELLERCHECKOUT (4YR BAY GELDING)

TRAINER:	Paul Nicholls
PEDIGREE:	Getaway – Loreley (Oscar)
FORM (P2P):	1 -
OPTIMUM TRIP:	2m 4f +
GOING:	Soft/Heavy

This son of Getaway could take time to come to hand.

The Dellercheckout came home alone on his debut in attritional conditions at Lismore in March, where three of his rivals pulled up and his only other challenger exited the race at the penultimate fence when holding every chance. It is impossible to say who would have won bar the fall, but The Dellercheckout clearly impressed Ryan Mahon and John Hales, who were prepared to part with £260,000 to acquire him at Cheltenham in March.

The four-year-old hails from the family of Avoca Promise and Champion Hurdle winners Morley Street and Granville Again.

He will be one to note when the mud is flying.

FIVE TO FOLLOW

The following five horses are the pick of my point-to-pointers to follow for the new season.

Blackbow (Willie Mullins) – there have been better point-to-point performances, but I loved him in the paddock at Aintree and have to include him here.

Cracking Destiny (Nicky Henderson) – I loved the attitude he displayed from the front. An honest type who should do well this season.

Dorrells Pierji (Willie Mullins) – posted a very good time despite not hitting top gear.

Global Citizen (Jonjo O'Neill) – a nice model of a horse and coasted through his point-to-point. He looks speedy.

Storm Control (Kerry Lee) – we probably won't see the best of this gelding until much later in his career, but he's a lovely stamp of a horse and won impressively.

TAKING A LOOK BACK

JODIE STANDING

My point-to-point feature from last year's *Dark Horses Jumps Guide* helped shine the light on a few decent winners as well as unearthing some potential top prospects for this coming season. Of the horses mentioned **Samcro** was probably the pick.

He won three bumpers in Ireland for Gordon Elliott including a Listed success and he looks set to make a big impact in the novice hurdle division this season. Providing everything goes smoothly I wouldn't be surprised to see him line up in the Neptune at the Cheltenham Festival in March.

Another talented individual who did well in bumpers was Brian Ellison's **Ravenhill Road**. He was last seen winning at Doncaster under a penalty in November and a campaign for the Champion Bumper was on the cards until the gelding met with a minor setback. Provided he returns sound this season he should reach a decent level over hurdles but, already a six-year-old, I wouldn't have thought it would be too long before he goes chasing.

One horse that did make the Cheltenham Festival was **Cause Toujours**. Dan Skelton's gelding scored impressively on his bumper debut at Warwick and went off a well-backed 9/2 favourite for the Champion Bumper in March.

A combination of inexperience and a rough passage probably contributed to his underperforming but the experience won't be lost on him and he has the potential to compete at the top level over hurdles.

Coastal Tiep was a horse I became quite fond of. Trained by Paul Nicholls to win a bumper before a novice hurdle event at

Kempton, he always struck me as an individual with plenty of ability but he was held back by greenness.

Nicholls may be keen to exploit a handicap mark of 134 over obstacles before sending him chasing. A step up to three miles could be on the cards providing he settles.

Another top novice chasing prospect for the Ditcheat trainer is **Topofthegame**.

This big gelding ran with great credit over hurdles, winning once before finishing fourth to Wholestone and then later a neck behind Beyond Conceit who went on to finish second to The Worlds End in the Grade 1 Sefton Novices' at Aintree. He is the type to keep on improving and could excel over the larger obstacles.

The less-exposed **Secret Investor** is also worth following providing he returns sound and well.

Of the others **Spiritofthegames** should be able to exploit a lenient handicap mark of 129.

He ran well to finish second in a competitive handicap hurdle event on Boxing Day at Kempton before winning by eight lengths back in novice company at Taunton.

Nicky Henderson's **Lough Derg Spirit** attained a decent level over timber before rounding off his campaign with a disappointing effort in the Grade 1 Mersey Novices' Hurdle at Aintree. A mark of 137 looks workable over 3m on good ground but his trainer may be tempted to send him over fences. He is not the biggest of horses but is very athletic.

Elegant Escape is set to embark on a chasing career and Colin Tizzard has spoken positively about how well he has summered. He won his first two starts over hurdles but fell short of Graded level later on in the season. Fences could be the making of him and I expect to see him thrive over two and a half and three miles.

Minella Warrior showed promise in two competitive bumpers. Not bred to be a speedy type, I expect to see him perform more prominently over hurdles.

Tacenda ran well enough in her bumper before trying her hand in a mares' novices' chase at Exeter. She was receiving plenty of weight but showed up well against the highly regarded Tagrita, staying on all the way to the line over an inadequate trip. She then picked up a small injury but her trainer says she is back in training and will be aimed at some decent staying handicap chases this season. She is definitely one to keep on the right side.

Over in Ireland **Judgement Day** for Henry De Bromhead is crying out for a step up in trip. He showed promise in all three starts but ultimately his future lies over fences.

Super Follo wasn't seen on a racecourse but remains one to follow with Noel Meade given his high-class point-to-point form.

the Weekend card

Informative and insightful news & views

Published weekly every Thursday containing news from our team.

Available through the post or to download

The Weekend Card is all about continuity, assuring our clients of feedback on our selections – win or lose.

Past copies are available to view online or by calling us and requesting a **free information pack**.

5 Issues £30: 10 Issues £55: 20 Issues £100: 30 Issues £145

Tel: 01539 741 007

Email: rebecca@martenjulian.com

www.martenjulian.com

THE 2018 CHAMPION HURDLE PREVIEW

MARTEN JULIAN

As I write this in late September the market for the 2018 Champion Hurdle is dominated by three horses – last year's winner Buveur D'Air, 2015 winner Faugheen and last season's impressive Triumph Hurdle winner Defi Du Seuil.

Of the three there are fewer doubts about Buveur D'Air than the other two, with Faugheen having to prove he is back to full fitness having not raced since January 2016, and Defi Du Seuil having the option of switching to novice chasing.

In this preview a year ago I advised **Buveur D'Air** for the Champion Hurdle at 25/1. However, the betting slip looked doomed for the bin when he returned in a novice chase at Haydock in December and beat the useful Cloudy Dream, then rated on 144, very comfortably by three and a quarter lengths.

Despite jumping well he was less convincing at Warwick a fortnight later and it was not long afterwards that the betting slip sprung back to life when Nicky Henderson announced that the horse would revert to hurdles with the Champion Hurdle as the main target.

The decision was understandable, as the Champion Hurdle picture was unclear with doubts about the wellbeing of Faugheen, while the Arkle Trophy market was dominated by Buveur D'Air's stable companion Altior who was, even by then, an odds-on chance for the race. Henderson may also have been influenced by the fact that Altior had beaten Buveur D'Air by eight and a half lengths in the 2016 Supreme Novices' Hurdle. In short, he probably knew Altior was the better horse.

Buveur D'Air duly returned to hurdling at Sandown in February, beating Rayvin Black by a length and a half in a 2m Listed contest in heavy ground. Rated on 151 at the time and in receipt of 4lb from the runner-up, he was entitled to beat an opponent rated 10lb inferior but he still won in good style, hard held and with what looked a ton in hand.

Buveur D'Air's next race was the Champion Hurdle, for which he started a relatively weak 5/1 chance with concerns that the ground may not be quite soft enough for him.

Buveur D'Air – sets the height of the bar

Under a confident ride from Noel Fehily and travelling smoothly throughout, he was settled in sixth for the first mile of the race, jumping slickly apart from clipping the top of the third last. Moving up into fourth, he was second turning for home and then pushed into the lead on the run to the last, holding the advantage to the line from the gallant My Tent Or Yours.

The time of the race was good – 3m 50.90, as opposed to Labaik's 3m 53.20 two hours earlier in the Supreme Novices' Hurdle.

Four weeks later Buveur D'Air confirmed his form with My Tent Or Yours, stepping up to two and a half miles for the Aintree Hurdle and beating the runner-up by five lengths eased down, with more in hand than at Cheltenham. This was another fluent round of jumping – he was especially good at the sixth, seventh and final flights – appearing to relish the longer trip as he powered home to the line.

Like many Champion Hurdle winners before him, Buveur D'Air is probably more suited to two and a half miles than the minimum trip. Cheltenham, especially when racing at festival pace, is ultimately a test of stamina and as a half-brother to top staying performer Punchestowns and 2m 6f winner Rackham Lerouge, from the family of a useful cross-country chaser, Buveur D'Air has a pedigree strongly biased towards stamina.

Although he has the potential to be top class over fences, Buveur D'Air is a slicker operator over hurdles. As his trainer says, his hurdling technique enables him to gain a length or two over his rivals through the race – something which he feels less likely over a fence.

The other factor to bear in mind is he is not a very big horse. That's not to say he is lacking physique, but upon seeing him it's easy to understand why he is so nimble and can jump hurdles with such alacrity.

Assuming he gets a clear run at the race, Buveur D'Air has to rank as the one to beat. He has only once finished out of the three, winning ten of his 13 starts, and the evidence from Aintree would suggest he is still improving. It now looks as if chasing is not on the agenda while there is uncertainty, for a variety of reasons, about those around him.

A top price of 4/1 – at this stage of the season – is about right about a horse who could, come the day, start at short odds to land the double. His claims are hard to fault.

The prevailing uncertainty of this season's Champion Hurdle relates to **Faugheen** – known by a few of his more devoted followers as 'The Machine'.

Owner Rich Ricci has said recently that 12 months ago Faugheen came back into training carrying plenty of weight and it proved difficult getting him back to full fitness. This autumn, in common with other members of his string, he has returned looking far better.

It is, though, a long time since Faugheen has been seen on the track.

We didn't see him at any stage of last season and despite missing the major festivals in the spring of 2016 he still ended that campaign as the highest-rated hurdler in Britain and Ireland with a mark of 176. This was due, in the main, to his 15-lengths defeat of Arctic Fire, with Nichols Canyon a further 13 lengths away in third, in the BHP Insurances Irish Champion Hurdle at Leopardstown in January of that year.

Ruby Walsh likes to keep things simple when riding Faugheen, electing to dominate from the front when he can. The only time in recent starts that he did not set the pace was when he was beaten at Punchestown.

In the 2015 Champion Hurdle he immediately went into the lead, settling well. Faugheen has always had a tendency to clip the top of the occasional hurdle and he did here, at the third,

Faugheen – can 'The Machine' return to full fitness?

but it didn't cost him any ground and he was still travelling well when joined on the approach to the second-last by Jezki and The New One.

Just as it looked as if he could be in trouble he pulled away on the run to the final flight before holding the determined late surge of stable companion Arctic Fire by a length and a half. Faugheen increased that margin of superiority over the runner-up to eight lengths on his final start in the Punchestown Champion Hurdle in May.

Faugheen's sole defeat in 13 lifetime starts came on his return to action at Punchestown in November 2015, where he went down by half a length to stable companion Nichols Canyon in the Morgiana Hurdle. The way he hung there may have been a consequence of the back trouble he is said to have suffered in the past, although that was not put forward as an excuse by connections afterwards. Whatever the reason the horse was clearly not at ease with himself.

He returned to winning ways at Kempton on Boxing Day 2015, when he made all to beat The New One in the Christmas Hurdle before that scintillating defeat of Arctic Fire at Leopardstown just less than a month later. He has not raced since.

Faugheen is blessed with a formidable pair of attributes – stamina and a turn of foot. His ability to change gear enables him to power clear of his rivals, while he has stamina to call upon for that final surge to the line.

It's not easy trying to tie in his form with the 2017 Champion Hurdle, but a tenuous line through The New One – beaten about eight lengths by Faugheen in 2015 and again by seven on Boxing Day that same year – would suggest that Buveur D'Air is a length or two superior.

Regarding the future there is little chance that Faugheen will be risked over fences as a nine-year-old, especially in the light of his recent setbacks. It is possible that connections may consider stepping Faugheen back up in trip – he won over three miles as a novice and landed the 2014 Neptune Hurdle over two miles five furlongs. I expect that to depend on what else is around at the time.

However it is very likely that the Champion Hurdle will be the main target.

His age is no barrier to him winning next spring – Sea Pigeon won it as a 10- and 11-year-old, albeit a long time ago – but Faugheen is an exceptional talent and he is lightly raced, with just 13 runs to his name.

An early spin in the Morgiana Hurdle or Hatton's Grace is apparently the plan and if that goes smoothly I would expect him to be vying for favouritism. It's probably fair to say that his current odds of 8/1 are based more on the bookmakers following that tried and tested maxim that 'they don't come back' than the horse's credentials on form.

Defi Du Seuil – running up that hill

Defi Du Seuil, trained by Philip Hobbs, has to rank as one of the toughest juvenile hurdlers to race in recent seasons.

He must have a constitution made of iron to have won seven races on the bounce, taking on tougher opposition each time and culminating in victories in the Triumph Hurdle and ending with a defeat of Divin Bere in the Grade 1 Doom Bar Anniversary Juvenile Hurdle at Aintree.

Following a second and a win in three-year-old bumpers in France in the spring of 2016, he made his hurdling debut for Philip Hobbs at Ffos Las in October, beating Ochos Rios to win easily by five lengths. Just under a month later he beat Diable De Sivola by one and three-quarter lengths at Cheltenham before returning there in December to beat Coeur De Lion by a length and three-quarters.

His next target was the Grade 1 Finale Hurdle at Chepstow, where despite clattering through the third and second last he galloped on strongly to the line to beat Evening Hush by 13 lengths. Just over a month later it was back to Cheltenham for a Grade 2 contest and then came the Festival and Aintree.

The feature of his performance in the Triumph Hurdle was the manner in which he quickened twice, first approaching the last and then again on the run-in – said by wise heads to be the mark of a very special horse.

Described by Barry Geraghty as being 'on springs', Defi Du Seuil is generally a slick jumper. The mistakes he made in the straight at Chepstow were out of character, possibly in part due to his losing concentration after being left out alone in the lead for too long. He had no trouble at all handling the hustle and bustle of the 15-runner field in the Triumph Hurdle.

Defi Du Seuil has everything you could wish for in a potential Champion Hurdle winner. The only thing that may deter people is his age, as the last five-year-old to win the race was Katchit in 2008 and before that See You Then, who won the first of his three Champion Hurdles in 1985. Night Nurse, not unlike Defi Du Seuil in constitution, won the race aged five in 1976.

Defi Du Seuil has apparently summered well, arriving back in the yard in August. The Fighting Fifth, where he would escape a penalty, has been mentioned as a possible target with Cheltenham's International Hurdle another option.

With doubts about Faugheen, the 8/1 available as I write in late September represents fair value. Philip Hobbs has already said the Champion Hurdle will be the target, assuming all goes well in his preparatory races.

Obviously we need to see how Defi Du Seuil matches up with the older generation of hurdlers, but on the evidence to hand he is hard to fault. He has that rare blend of courage to match his ability.

Plans for **Yorkhill** are undecided and may remain so for a time to come.

This winner of nine of his 11 starts was confined to chasing last season, winning three including the JLT Novices' Chase at Cheltenham and ending with a neck defeat by Road To Respect a month later at Fairyhouse after conceding ground by jumping left throughout the race.

The last time we saw Yorkhill over hurdles he finished fourth in the Grade 1 Champion Novice Hurdle at Punchestown in April 2016. That followed a run of four successes at Punchestown, Sandown, a defeat of Yanworth in the Neptune Novices' Hurdle and then a win over two and a half miles in Grade 1 company at Aintree.

A mark of 154 over hurdles leaves Yorkhill 15lb adrift of Buveur D'Air, but Willie Mullins went out of his way to suggest a return to hurdling as an option last spring. Lines through the horses he has met over hurdles – Yanworth, Brain Power and Petit Mouchoir – would, though, suggest he has ground to find with Buveur D'Air.

It would not be beyond the realms of possibility that **Douvan** reverts to hurdling.

Owner Rich Ricci was speculating about the horse taking a step up in trip when talking this autumn, perhaps swayed by the prospect of having to meet Altior if he stayed over two miles and fences.

The last time we saw him over hurdles he beat no less a horse than Sizing John in the Grade 1 Herald Champion Novice Hurdle at Punchestown by seven and a half lengths.

Things evidently were not right when he was beaten at odds of 2/9 in the Queen Mother Champion Chase, but that followed a succession of nine victories, again beating Sizing John on no fewer than four of those occasions.

Douvan kept better company over hurdles than stable companion Yorkhill and at the age of eight he is young enough to adapt. If the Champion Hurdle starts to cut up then the option of a switch back to hurdling would be a perfectly reasonable consideration.

That poor performance in the Queen Mother Champion Chase may have left its mark, in which case a return to hurdling would make perfect sense.

Apple's Jade is a remarkable mare. She is the winner of seven of her 11 starts as a hurdler – five of them in Grade 1 company – with her four most recent outings coming over two and a half miles.

She showed she has the courage to match her ability when battling bravely to get the better of Vroum Vroum Mag and Limini in the OLBG Mares' Hurdle at last year's Festival. Six weeks later she looked even better when defeating Airlie Beach by 14 lengths in the Grade 1 Mares Champion Hurdle at Punchestown.

Apple's Jade – winner of five Grade 1 races

There was talk of her running in last year's Champion Hurdle, but Gordon Elliott advised the owners that she would be 'taken off her feet' in that company.

Things may be different this time, especially if she shapes well in the trials.

Min enjoyed a tall reputation until he was firmly put in his place by Altior in the 2016 Supreme Novices' Hurdle.

He impressed with his jumping in two starts over fences before Christmas and I would expect him to stay chasing this season, with the Queen Mother Champion Chase a possible target if Douvan, who runs in the same colours, heads elsewhere.

Rich Ricci and Willie Mullins can also call upon **Limini**.

The daughter of Peintre Celebre was beaten eight and a quarter lengths by Buveur D'Air at Aintree in 2016 but beat Apple's Jade by a couple of lengths at Punchestown last February before failing to confirm that form at the Cheltenham Festival. The six-year-old is held on various lines of form but she may come into the reckoning if connections are struggling with their main contenders.

Melon was very well regarded last season but had his limitations exposed when runner-up to Labaik in the Supreme Novices' Hurdle and again next time at Punchestown. Novice chases look his best option.

Petit Mouchoir improved last season, landing the Grade 1 Ryanair Hurdle by seven lengths from Nichols Canyon at Leopardstown over Christmas and then beating Footpad by a length back there a month later. He ran the best race of his career when third to Buveur D'Air in the Champion Hurdle despite making a few mistakes and losing momentum, notably at the second last.

The grey does not need to find a great deal to make up the ground with Buveur D'Air and if he can improve his jumping there is every chance of his doing so.

Pingshou – may enter the Champion Hurdle reckoning

Wicklow Brave was beaten fourteen and a half lengths in last season's Champion Hurdle and despite running creditably on the Flat this summer it's hard to see him finding the necessary improvement to be competitive.

Pingshou, beaten 34 lengths by Labaik in the Supreme Novices' Hurdle, improved significantly on that effort when he beat the promising Mount Mews at Aintree in April. He confirmed he was still on an upward curve when ending the season with a fair third to Cilaos Emery and Melon in the Herald Champion Novice Hurdle at Punchestown.

One would have expected the seven-year-old to be sent chasing but his trainer Colin Tizzard was talking this autumn in terms of the Champion Hurdle. He will need to find at least a stone to become competitive with the best.

John Constable is worth keeping an eye on.

Trained in his younger days by Aidan O'Brien, he was competing in decent handicap hurdles by the end of his novice campaign in the spring of 2016 and last season ran in top handicaps before landing some hefty bets by 14 lengths in the Swinton Hurdle from a mark of 134. He then returned to action in July and defied a 16lb higher mark to beat Red Tornado in a Listed handicap hurdle at Market Rasen.

Now rated on 156, and aged just six, his form warrants respect as a long-range outsider for the race. He acts particularly well on good ground and odds of 50/1 underrate his chance.

There was quite a buzz about **Charli Parcs** last season.

The winner of a three-year-old hurdle in France in November, he beat Master Blueyes by eight lengths on his UK debut at Kempton over Christmas before falling two out back at the track in February. He was well supported for the Triumph Hurdle but didn't quicken from the home turn and finished sixth, beaten ten lengths by the winner.

Charli Parcs – the dark horse of the race

Although only a four-year-old there is talk of him tackling fences later in the season. He does, though, show plenty of ability in his work and an early trial will guide connections to the way forward.

CONCLUSION

It is hard to look beyond the front three as I write in the autumn.

Faugheen is undeniably attractively priced at 8/1 but those apparently generous odds are more a reflection of his chance of returning to full fitness rather than his claims on the book. There is also the possibility that he may be stepped back up in trip.

Buveur D'Air, at a top price of 4/1, warrants his place at the head of the market. He may not need to improve again to complete the double and there is no risk of him returning to chasing or competing in long-distance hurdles.

Defi Du Seuil looks very exciting. He showed exceptional tenacity to cope with a busy schedule last season and although unproven against the older generation, that turn of foot looks a potent weapon.

Watch for a possible return to hurdling for Douvan. Connections may decide the Champion Hurdle presents less of a challenge than tackling Altior, although that could be a late call on the part of connections.

Apple's Jade and Petit Mouchoir don't need to improve that much to figure, while John Constable has shown enough to warrant respect in what could be an open year.

Buveur D'Air sets a high standard with Defi Du Seuil snapping at his heels. John Constable, at 50/1, is the pick of the outsiders.

THE 2018 CHELTENHAM GOLD CUP PREVIEW

MARTEN JULIAN

This time a year ago a large cloud of uncertainty hung over the likely participants in the 2017 Gold Cup, and things don't seem to be that much clearer 12 months later.

There were serious doubts about the wellbeing of Coneygree and Don Cossack, winners of the race in 2015 and 2016 respectively, while the stamina of Vautour, Douvan and Cue Card was unproven over the Gold Cup trip. Then there was Thistlecrack who, this time a year ago, had not jumped a fence in public.

In the end I sided with Don Cossack, who never appeared, while to my shame and embarrassment the winner Sizing John failed to receive even a mention. It was that sort of year.

The current favourite, as I write in September, is **Thistlecrack** at a top price of 6/1.

There was a great deal of excitement about Thistlecrack's participation in last season's race, that was until his trainer Colin Tizzard informed the public on 20th February that he would not be running after a scan revealed that the horse had torn a tendon.

The latest news, as I write in September, is that Thistlecrack is sound and well having been ridden and kept hacking since the end of July. The plan is to give him two months of gentle road work and then a racecourse gallop in December before attempting a repeat victory in the King George VI Chase at Kempton.

Thistlecrack – high hopes for a return to full fitness

Thistlecrack was a top price of 15/8 for the Gold Cup at the time of his injury, as a consequence of a hugely impressive novice campaign over fences.

The 2016 World Hurdle winner won his first four starts over fences over an extended two miles seven furlongs at Chepstow, an extended three miles at Cheltenham, an extended two miles seven furlongs at Newbury and then most notably becoming the first novice chaser to win the King George VI Chase at Kempton, beating stable companion Cue Card by three and a quarter lengths.

The feature of that performance was a few spine-tingling leaps, at some fences taking off outside the wings. Cue Card, ridden by Paddy Brennan, tried to put him under pressure six fences out but Thistlecrack cruised away to go clear turning for home.

Everyone seemed very impressed by the nature of the victory, believing that the horse had more in hand than the three and a quarter lengths winning margin would suggest.

Yet to my eyes Thistlecrack was a little tired on the run to the line, despite Tom Scudamore easing down and allowing himself the opportunity to salute the crowd approaching the post.

Up until that point Thistlecrack had never run beyond an extended three miles. That was to come two months later when he tackled an extended three miles one furlong in Cheltenham's BetBright Trial Cotswold Chase. Such was his reputation that he started 4/9 to beat the more experienced and proven Many Clouds, rated just 5lb inferior, and the 163-rated Smad Place.

On this occasion his performance was marred by a couple of sloppy jumps, at the ninth and three fences from home. He was then ridden strongly at the last and despite responding bravely was held close home by the gallant Many Clouds, who tragically collapsed and died due to a pulmonary haemorrhage after the race.

On this occasion Thistlecrack did not appear to stay the trip as well as the winner, at least not in the soft ground, despite having a pedigree that could not be more endowed with stamina, being by Kayf Tara out of a mare by Ardross and from a family of strong stayers.

We know that Thistlecrack has the class to win a Gold Cup and, on good ground, he would probably get home. There is, however, a lingering doubt on that score, especially if the going should be testing, while we also need to see evidence that he has fully recovered from injury.

The other concern – and this is a personal observation from someone who was unceremoniously unseated from a horse at no more than a trot on the sole occasion he took to the saddle – is that Tom Scudamore and Thistlecrack do not always seem to be in perfect harmony.

Put simply, there have been occasions when the horse looks to have taken control. This was especially noticeable in the King George, where Thistlecrack took off outside the wings at the open ditches (2nd and 11th fences) and then later when Cue Card moved up alongside, forcing him into a duel for a few strides.

The partnership has, though, been successful in all but two of their dozen races together and Tom Scudamore knows the horse well enough to appreciate when the time is right to let Thistlecrack have his way.

As for the betting perspective, until more is known and we see that the horse is back on the track he cannot be recommended for ante-post purposes at his current price.

I have to admit that I never expected **Sizing John** to win last year's race. Not only that, he became the first horse in history to win the Irish Gold Cup, Cheltenham Gold Cup and Punchestown Gold Cup in the same season.

I respected his consistency and progressive profile going into the race, having risen from a mark of 150, when he appeared at Christmas, to 167 by Cheltenham, but I emphatically belonged in the camp that believed he would not stay.

Most of his family have shown their best form over two and a half miles or thereabouts and his maternal grandsire Northern Crystal's trip was up to a mile.

Furthermore, the seven-year-old had occasionally raced keenly, as was the case when he beat Empire Of Dirt by a hard-fought three-quarters of a length over an extended three miles in the Irish Gold Cup in February. That form, against a rival rated 4lb inferior, didn't look good enough.

Jessica Harrington – hoping for another tremendous season

Come the big day Sizing John travelled well throughout, making headway four fences from home and quickening discernibly to lead soon after the second last. About three lengths up over the final fence, he stayed on in determined fashion to beat the strong-finishing Minella Rocco by two and three-quarter lengths, with Native River and Djakadam close behind in third and fourth. At the line he was comfortably in control.

The victory owed a great deal to the judgement of his rider Robbie Power, who advised Jessica Harrington from the horse's homework and victory at Leopardstown that 'all he did was stay'. He added that because of his speed over two miles he was able to 'take him back and fill him up' through the course of the race. The good ground also played a major part in the race, perhaps putting a greater emphasis on speed than stamina.

Just over a month later Sizing John met Djakadam again in the Punchestown Gold Cup, not travelling as well as he did at Cheltenham but still keeping on very gamely under a strong ride to beat him by a short head, with Coneygree a length and a half back in third. The flatter track and shorter trip probably attributed to the reduced margin between him and Djakadam but this was a victory that owed much to the winner's tenacity after the last.

By contrast with the impression made before Cheltenham, Sizing John looked here as if this return to an extended three miles did not offer sufficient a test for him. What it did establish, though, is that Sizing John is an incredibly tough horse and furthermore he was and probably is still improving.

On known form, and given a clean bill of health, Sizing John should be heading the Gold Cup market. Although he has been successful on soft ground, he would probably always prefer better going.

The concern is that the horse had an incredibly hard season, especially in the spring. He never makes winning look easy, and it will be interesting to see if those tough races have left their mark. I actually think that unlikely, but it's something to bear in mind.

The intention is to start him off in the Betfair Chase at Haydock in November and have a crack at the £1 million bonus for winning there, the King George and the Gold Cup.

Jessica Harrington has another strong contender with **Our Duke**.

The son of Oscar is lightly raced, having run just nine times, but he has won five and never finished out of the frame in eight completed outings.

A bumper winner on his debut in November 2015, a month later he ran the useful Death Duty to half a length trying to concede 3lb in a Listed bumper at Navan before making a successful hurdling debut at Leopardstown the following January.

Our Duke – more than just a galloper

His first try over fences in public resulted in a victory over two and a half miles at Navan in December, followed by a half-length defeat of Coney Island over three miles later that month at Leopardstown.

He then went down by a length and three-quarters to Disko over an extended two miles five furlongs back there in February, after a number of mistakes, before showing that stamina was his strong suit when beating Bless The Wings by 14 lengths over three miles five furlongs in the Irish Grand National at Fairyhouse in April – a victory that saw his rating raised a stone from 153 to 167, just 1lb below Sizing John.

The trainer says she will try and keep the two horses apart until March, with Our Duke the more likely to tackle the long-distance staying chasers in the midwinter ground.

Our Duke is not just a strong galloper – his form over shorter trips proves that – but his proven stamina is a massive advantage in the Gold Cup which, essentially, favours the stayers.

One of the most exciting new faces to emerge into the Gold Cup picture last season was **Might Bite**, a son of Scorpion who had won three of his four starts over hurdles culminating in a mark of 148.

He did not make an immediate impact over fences, finishing fifth of seven to More Of That at Cheltenham in November 2015, and then returning to fences a year later at Ffos Las, beaten at odds of 2/1 on in a three-horse race.

A victory over two miles three furlongs around Doncaster in December did wonders for his confidence and he was about to run out a clear-cut winner of the Kauto Star Novices' Chase at Kempton on Boxing Day until falling, arguably through no fault of his own, when about 20 lengths clear at the last.

Might Bite – talented but the character to match

He then made light work of landing the odds over three miles back at Doncaster before beating stable companion Whisper by a nose in the RSA Novices' Chase at Cheltenham, almost forfeiting the race when idling and veering right on the run-in before regaining the lead close home.

He ended the campaign when confirming the form with the runner-up the following month at Aintree, making all to win by two lengths.

Might Bite is not straightforward, as we saw in the RSA, but Nico De Boinville rides him with great sensitivity and that will continue to be the way forward. A half-brother to the same stable's Beat That, he was not stopping over three miles and a furlong at Aintree and is bred to stay further.

It does, though, seem from trainer Nicky Henderson's comments that the King George is viewed as the horse's primary target this season, although if he were to win there I have no doubt the Gold Cup would come into the picture.

A mark of 162 leaves Might Bite a few pounds behind his main rivals, but he is a horse of immense talent with the potential to progress further. He is well suited by good ground.

It says something for the strength of the new order that only now does Willie Mullins get a name-check. His three leading candidates at this time are Yorkhill, Douvan and Djakadam.

Djakadam will probably have the race as his target for a fourth successive year, having run second to Coneygree in 2015 and Don Cossack in 2016 and then fourth to Sizing John last March.

For all his consistency Djakadam has looked a weak finisher at Cheltenham.

The trainer had been particularly hopeful for his chance last season, stressing that he had enjoyed a trouble-free preparation, and indeed he did look the winner from the back straight only to again find less than expected and 'empty' from the last, fading close home to finish fourth.

The finish of the 2017 Gold Cup

He then ran Sizing John to a short head in that epic battle for the Punchestown Gold Cup, reducing the three and a quarter lengths' deficit at Cheltenham due to the flatter track and quarter mile shorter trip.

Djakadam, an eight-year-old, will still be a relatively young horse in March but connections may be more inclined to aim him at the King George, where the flatter track and shorter trip will play more to his strengths.

Djakadam has as much class as any staying chaser around and it would be churlish to crab his consistent record at the highest level. It would not surprise anyone to see him figure again next March but it would be equally surprising if there were not a couple too good for him. Put succinctly, he just doesn't seem to get along with the place.

Douvan went into last year's Festival unbeaten in nine starts over fences.

Starting 9/2 on for the Queen Mother Champion Chase, he hit the third last fence and found nothing to finish seventh having been eased up in the closing stages. There had been early indications in the race when he overjumped that all was not well, and the horse was subsequently found to be lame.

Douvan has to prove that he can recapture his former level. If he does then his participation in the Gold Cup will probably be dependent on the quality of opposition around in the Queen Mother Champion Chase, notably in relation to Altior.

Regarding Douvan's stamina, his sire Walk In The Park gets winners at most trips but his dam's family were at their most effective around two miles.

Having said that, Douvan is probably the most innately talented horse that Rich Ricci has ever owned, and given his bold and attacking policy the Gold Cup is likely to come in for consideration if all goes well in the interim.

The team's best hope from last year's novice ranks is **Yorkhill**, a winner of both his bumpers and then four of his five starts over hurdles including a one and three-quarter length defeat of Yanworth in the 2016 Neptune Investment Management Novices' Hurdle.

Douvan – will he tackle Altior or be trained for the Gold Cup?

He made a belated return to action at Fairyhouse in December, winning a 2m beginners chase with great ease before landing a Grade 3 just over a month later over two miles three furlongs at Leopardstown.

He then came to Cheltenham for the JLT Novices' Chase, travelling well and responding to firm driving to beat Top Notch by a length, and ended the season with a neck defeat by Road To Respect over two and a half miles at Fairyhouse, a race he would have won but for forfeiting a considerable amount of ground by jumping left.

Although Willie Mullins was thinking in terms of the Champion Hurdle for Yorkhill after he won the Neptune, and again after his final start last season, my preference would be to see him stepped up to three miles as a chaser. His pedigree has the requisite stamina, by the late Presenting out of an unraced daughter of Saddlers' Hall related to staying performers Offshore Account and Dooneys Gate, from the family of Fork Lightning and The Listener.

Yorkhill – quirky but talented

This is very sound staying blood, and furthermore the horse runs as if he will get beyond three miles.

Yorkhill will be Andrea and Graham Wylie's best chance of a Gold Cup runner next season so there should not be any conflict of interest with other horses in the yard. He is, though, also quoted for the Champion Hurdle and is not without his quirks. He fell in a schooling session at Leopardstown before Cheltenham and can be very keen.

It is my belief that **Native River** might have won the Gold Cup if the ground had been riding softer.

This admirably consistent seven-year-old has finished in the frame in all his 11 starts over fences, winning six of them. He ended his novice chasing campaign with a good second to Minella Rocco in the 2016 National Hunt Chase at Cheltenham followed in April by a comfortable defeat of Henri Parry Morgan in the Grade 1 Mildmay Novices' Chase at Aintree.

Following a pipe-opener over hurdles he landed the Hennessy Gold Cup from a mark of 155 and then the Welsh Grand National over an extended three miles five furlongs. He dropped back to a trip just short of three miles to beat Le Mercurey in the Denman Chase before lining up for the Gold Cup just over a month later.

Having won his six starts over fences on going described as good to soft, or softer, there were concerns beforehand that the good ground might find him out. In the event he ran a stormer, up there most of the way and responding with the utmost courage from the second last to remain competitive all the way to the line. It was only in the last stride that he was caught for second, finishing two and three-quarter lengths behind the winner.

Of the 13 runners in the Gold Cup, Native River did the most work having had plenty of use made of him throughout. Only a horse of exceptional courage could have battled back into contention in the way that he did.

Native River – admirably tough and consistent

As an eight-year-old next March, Native River will line up as one of the youngest but most experienced horses in the field. It is my view that last season's good ground on Gold Cup day would have suited the winner far better than Native River – certainly sufficient to account for the 3lb that separated them on the day.

Native River makes great appeal at 12/1 because he is a very sound jumper, extremely consistent and still progressing. Furthermore, his rating of 166 is just 2lb adrift of Sizing John.

Richard Johnson's bold style of riding, especially on the approach to the fences, suits the horse ideally. Trainer Colin Tizzard says the horse was a little bit 'shaken up' after the Gold Cup so he will not be out until around Christmas so that he is fresher for the second half of the season. He may also have the Grand National as a target if all goes smoothly at Cheltenham. There is much to like about him.

Jonjo O'Neill is aiming last year's Gold Cup runner-up **Minella Rocco** at the race again.

The plan is to go to Ireland in October and then tackle the Betfair Chase before heading to Cheltenham.

It is surprising that a horse of his ability has won just one of his nine starts over fences. Mind you that turned out to be top form, when in the 2016 National Hunt Chase he beat Native River by one and a quarter lengths over four miles.

The steady pace at which last season's Gold Cup was run did not play to the strengths of this confirmed stayer, who made up about ten lengths from the last fence and was never nearer than at the line.

Minella Rocco evidently likes Cheltenham and with stamina assured he appeals as the sort of horse that could make the frame again.

Minella Rocco – an out-and-out stayer

Stable companion **More Of That**, winner of the 2014 World Hurdle, shaped well in sixth in the Gold Cup before pulling up in the Grand National, apparently suffering from a fibrillating heart condition. Rated 159, 8lb below his hurdle mark, the nine-year-old has the race as his long-term target. He had unseated his rider at the last fence in the Irish Gold Cup, won by Sizing John. He does, though, need to improve to win the race and at the age of ten next March, others may be progressing faster.

Coneygree has the £250,000 Ladbrokes Trophy – the race formerly known as the Hennessy – at Newbury on 2 December as his first major target. Nico De Boinville gave the horse one of the best judged rides I have ever seen at Cheltenham to win the 2015 Gold Cup, where he beat Djakadam by a length and a half, but injury has restricted him to just three runs since.

Last season started with a 25-lengths defeat of Seventh Sky at Sandown and then 11 days later he was well outpointed by Cue Card in the Betfair Chase at Haydock. He then made a belated return to the fray at the end of the season, running a blinder to finish a length and a half third to Sizing John and Djakadam in the Punchestown Gold Cup at the end of April.

Given that was his first run since November, and against two horses that had fought out the Gold Cup, this must rank as a performance of enormous merit. Indeed, if you assume that he might have needed the race, there is a strong case for suggesting he could find the couple of pounds required to reverse the form with the front two.

Against that he will be 11 next March and there is the question of his soundness. However, on the evidence from Punchestown he looked as good as ever and a clear run could see him lining up again with a serious chance.

Looking to the longer-priced contenders, **Whisper** may be allowed to take his chance. His proximity to Might Bite in the

RSA and then Aintree entitles him to respect although I don't see him as a serious contender.

Apparently **Cue Card** is being aimed at the race again despite falling in successive years, on both occasions at the third last fence from home.

There was much discussion following his 2016 mishap about whether he would have won, whereas last March he looked held at the time of his departure.

Last November he seemed better than ever when beating Coneygree by 15 lengths in the Betfair Chase before running Thistlecrack to three and a quarter lengths at Kempton. He then left the strong impression that the drop in trip suited him when beating Shantou Flyer by 15 lengths in the 2m 5f Ascot Chase and his season ended with a neck defeat by Tea For Two over 3m 1f at Aintree.

There were upbeat reports from the Tizzard camp about Cue Card in September, with a programme comprising a return at Wetherby, then the Betfair Chase, King George and Gold Cup. Much as I respect his record at the highest level it is hard to imagine him improving at the age of 12. There are, though, more good races to come along the way.

Fox Norton may give the Tizzards yet another string to their bow.

The son of Lando has made giant strides over the last two seasons, formerly with Neil Mulholland, running Special Tiara to a head in the Queen Mother Champion Chase at Cheltenham before beating Sub Lieutenant by six lengths over 2m 4f at Aintree and then putting up a career-best effort to beat Un De Sceaux in the BoyleSports Champion Chase at Punchestown in April. By the spring Fox Norton was looking more a stayer than a two-mile specialist, powering up the hill in the Queen Mother Champion Chase and surging away at the end of two and a half miles at Aintree.

Fox Norton – will he stay the Gold Cup trip?

The trainer said after Aintree that he thought Fox Norton would become a King George contender but added that owners Ann and Alan Potts would not be keen for him to clash with Sizing John.

Despite the impressions he left, on pedigree Fox Norton is not certain to stay three miles – his dam is related to milers from the family of an Irish 1,000 Guineas winner – but his style of racing promises that he could. If he were to win the King George then the Gold Cup would obviously come up for discussion. At 50/1 he is not without appeal.

Tea For Two atoned for rather ungallantly ditching Lizzie Kelly on the deck in front of the stands at the second fence in the Gold Cup when inflicting a neck defeat on Cue Card in the 3m 1f Betway Bowl at Aintree. Rated 12lb inferior to the runner-up before the race, the eight-year-old travelled smoothly throughout and after leading between the last two always looked like holding on.

This imposing son of Kayf Tara, who looked in superb condition in the paddock at Aintree, has the scope to progress having run just nine times over fences, winning four. He had been fancied to run well at Cheltenham – the trainer's wife Jane Williams says he was spot on for that race – and taking a line through Smad Place and, indirectly, Cue Card, but for his mishap he might have finished within a few lengths of the main contenders.

His earlier form in the King George, when he was a highly creditable fourth beaten three and a half lengths by Thistlecrack and just a neck behind Cue Card, would endorse that view.

Tea For Two was improving last season, as reflected by his mark, and the 50/1 available in places – much larger on the exchanges – underrates his chance. On form alone, within a pound or two of Thistlecrack and Cue Card, he commands far more respect than that price suggests.

Disko, winner of three of his six starts over fences, has the scope to become a contender. Aged just six, he won over 2m 4f at Punchestown in October and then reversed the form with Our Duke in the Grade 1 Flogas Novice Chase at Leopardstown before running a four-lengths third to Yorkhill in the JLT Novices' Chase at Cheltenham. His season ended on a high with a comfortable five-lengths defeat of Anibale Fly in the Grade 1 Growise Champion Novice Chase over an extended three miles at Punchestown in April.

Disko had apparently been working very well prior to the Punchestown race and there is no doubt he was improving fast last spring. The Gold Cup would be a possible target for him and as a seven-year-old next March he probably has more still to offer, but the shorter Ryanair may suit him better.

Min may enter the reckoning. The six-year-old son of Walk In The Park has always enjoyed a tall reputation in the Mullins' yard but he couldn't live with Altior when beaten seven lengths by him in the 2016 Supreme Novices' Hurdle.

Last season he ran twice over fences, winning both times, but he can be keen and makes more appeal as a two-mile specialist.

Everything seems to come alike to the remarkably versatile **Vroum Vroum Mag**. In the first three in all but one of her 21 starts, she is unbeaten in six runs over fences and has won at trips ranging from a mile and a half to three miles. At last year's Festival she took her place in the Mares' Hurdle, running Apple's Jade to a length and a half. Her last race over fences was when she won at Clonmel in November 2015.

Running plans for Rich Ricci's team will have much to do with what else he has around, but the mare has been mentioned in the context of the Gold Cup before and aged nine next spring, with plenty of experience at the top level, she could well take her chance in the line-up.

A mention has to be made for **American**, a talented but very fragile seven-year-old trained by Harry Fry.

He won his three starts over fences in increasingly impressive fashion, at Exeter and Warwick and then a 3m novices' handicap chase at Uttoxeter from a mark of 148. A 9lb rise to 157 leaves him with something to find, and soft ground is a prerequisite of his running anywhere, but this upwardly mobile son of Malinas is one of the most promising young chasers in training. I am expecting great things of him.

Empire Of Dirt's proximity to Sizing John in the Irish Gold Cup at Leopardstown in February, and then a good run behind Un De Sceaux in the Ryanair, puts him within a few pounds of the best. He has won a handicap chase at the 2016 Festival so clearly Cheltenham holds no fears for him. He will, though, be 11 next spring and he pulled up behind Tea For Two at Aintree when last seen in April.

Road To Respect, also owned by Gigginstown Stud, looks a more likely contender.

Aged just six, he beat Baron Alco by six lengths in the Grade 3 handicap chase over an extended two and a half miles at Cheltenham from a mark of 145 and then took advantage of Yorkhill's wayward jumping when beating him by a neck at Fairyhouse in April.

A rating of 157 leaves him 11lb adrift of Sizing John but he is bred to stay well – his dam is a half-sister to 3m hurdle and chase winner Road To Riches – and he has youth on his side. I see no reason why the Gold Cup should not be a long-term target and he acts well on good ground. There are worse 33/1 chances for the race.

Cloudy Dream was making giant strides last spring, ending the season with fine runs behind Altior in the Arkle Trophy, a one-length defeat by the resurgent Flying Angel at Aintree and a victory in a Grade 2 chase at Ayr.

Cloudy Dream's pedigree is inconclusive regarding his stamina limitations, but the impression is he would be best kept to two and a half miles or thereabouts.

Cloudy Dream – sure to make further progress

CONCLUSION

Of the more obvious contenders, we need to see evidence that Thistlecrack is back safe and sound but there is still that nagging doubt about the trip. Sizing John is incredibly tough but the good ground came right for him last year and that may be important over the trip. Yorkhill and Might Bite have talent to burn but neither is straightforward.

Our Duke is more than a galloper but needs to prove he can handle the step up to this level. Douvan could enter the reckoning if connections decide on an attacking policy but stable companion Djakadam is probably best kept to alternative targets after three attempts at the race. The same comment may apply to Cue Card. Coneygree needs to show he is back to full fitness. Tea For Two is overpriced on his bare form.

Native River looks a thoroughly safe pair of hands and is being kept fresh for a spring campaign. Minella Rocco is the sort of horse who could come right on the day while Fox Norton would make great appeal at 50/1 if, as I think likely, he stays the trip. Vroum Vroum Mag and Road To Respect are also worth a look.

To conclude, I like Native River each-way at 12/1. Next best are Minella Rocco at 16/1 and Fox Norton at 50/1.

INDEX

Air Navigator 27-28
American 154-155
Annamix 28
Antey 28-29
Apple's Jade 130-131
Ataguiseamix 75-76
Ballymoy 76-77
Battleoverdoyen 77
Better Getalong 29-30
Big River 30-31
Blackbow 78-79, 116
Brewin'Upastorm 79-80
Bullionaire 31-32
Burrows Saint 32
Buveur D'Air 121-124
Captain McGarry 33
Carefully Selected 80-81
Catwells 34
Cause Toujours 117
Chacun Pour Soi 34
Champ 35
Chapel Stile 65-66
Charli Parcs 133-134
Chooseyourweapon 81-82
Claimantakinforgan 35-36
Cloudy Dream 155-156

Coastal Tiep 117-118
Coneygree 150
Conquer Gold 66-67
Cool Getaway 82 83
Copper Gone West 83
Court Liability 84
Cracking Destiny 85, 116
Cue Card 151
Dame De Compagnie 36-37
Daphne Du Clos 37-38
Debece 9-10
Defi Du Seuil 127-128
Delirant 38
Demopolis 39
Disko 153-154
Diva Reconce 39
Djakadam 143-144
Dorrells Pierji 86, 116
Dostal Phil 40
Douvan 129-130, 144-145
Du Soleil 40-41
Elegant Escape 119
Ellens Way 67
Empire Of Dirt 155
Epicuris 41-42
Faugheen 124-126

Felix Desjy 87

Forgot To Ask 42

Fox Norton 151-153

Glenmona 88

Global Citizen 89, 116

Good Man Pat 90

Grey Mist 43

Gumball 43-44

Heroesandvillains 90-91

Hitman Fred 91-92

Indian Hawk 93

Jerrysback 44

Jet Set 45

John Constable 133

Judgement Day 119

Juge Et Parti 45-46

Just Minded 10-11

Just Your Type 46

Kings Monarch 94-95

Kupatana 95-96

Lad Of Luck 47

Lastbutnotleast 12-13

Limini 131

Lisdoonvarna Lad 47-48

Lord Ballim 68

Lough Derg Spirit 13-15, 119

Madison To Monroe 96-97

Mahari 48

Maire Benrigh 97-98

Melon 131

Midnight Maestro 69-70

Might Bite 142-143

Min 131, 154

Minella Rocco 149

Minella Warrior 119

Mon Port 49

Monbeg Zena 98 99

Monty's Award 49-50

Moonshine Bay 99-100

More Of That 150

Mount Mews 15-16

Mr Lingo 100-101

Native River 147-148

Net De Treve 101-102

Nietzsche 70-71

Not That Fuisse 16-18

On A Promise 71-72

On The Blind Side 102-103

Our Duke 140-141

Outofthisworld 50

Palmers Hill 103-104

Petit Mouchoir 131

Pingshou 132
Pontresina 104-105
Pop Rockstar 72
Posh Trish 105
Potterman 18
Quick Pick 51
Ravenhill Road 19, 117
Rio Quinto 51-52
Road To Respect 155
Run To Milan 52
Salsaretta 53
Sam Brown 20
Samcro 21, 117
Santini 106
Sao 53-54
Secret Investor 118
Senatus 54-55
Sending Love 107
Sharjah 55
Sizing John 138-140
Slate House 108
Sneaky Feeling 55-56
Some Man 109
Spiritofthegames 119
Stay Humble 110-111

Storm Control 111-112, 116
Storm Home 56, 112-113
Stormy Milan 57
Strong Pursuit 57-58
Super Follo 119
Sympa Des Flos 58-59
Tacenda 119
Tea For Two 22-24, 153
Templepark 113-115
Tetraites Style 59
The Big Bite 60
The Dellercheckout 115
Thistlecrack 135-138
Topofthegame 118
Un Noble 73
Uncle Alastair 60-61
Vroum Vroum Mag 154
Waiting Patiently 24-25
War Sound 61-62
What About Carlo 73-74
Whisper 150-151
Who's My Jockey 63
Wicklow Brave 132
Winter Soldier 63
Yorkhill 129, 145-147